Peter

from

Aardvark

Z*to*ebra

Secrets of African Wildlife

AUTHOR'S NOTE

From Aardvark to Zebra is an easy-to-read little 'dictionary' containing about 120 entries which, together, range across the spectrum of wildlife in the wider sense of the word – from southern Africa's mammals and birds through reptiles, fish and insects to trees and flowers. I have not tried to be comprehensive in terms of either the overall scope of the book or the information given in individual profiles: the animals and plants that appear in these pages were chosen, from an enormous number of possible inclusions, simply for the interest I feel they have for the casual browser and the ordinary, non-specialist reader. Similarly, the narrative itself, written for the layman rather than the scientist, focuses on just one or two features – the more intriguing ones – of each subject.

Several people helped in one way or another with the preparation of the book, among them Bill Branch, Mike Hoffmann, Norman Larsen, Peter Ryan, Ian Sinclair, Braam van Wyk and Alan Weaving – each an expert in his particular field. I am most grateful to them for their guidance and courtesy.

from

Aardvark

to

Zebra

AARDVARK

Orycteropus afer

The aardvark is one of the world's odder looking animals. About 1,5 metres long and 50 kilograms in weight, it has a long, pig-like snout, rabbit-like ears, a distinctly humped back, an apparently hairless skin and a 30-centimetre long tongue used to lap up the ants and termites on which it feeds.

It is also among the most accomplished diggers of the African veld, using its short, powerful front limbs and clawed feet to fashion its spacious and sometimes deep burrow in double-quick time. The home, which the animal tends to abandon fairly soon after moving in, is often taken over by another mammal (or bird, or snake).

Ants and termites, and especially the former, make up nearly the whole of the aardvark's diet. Having ripped open the nest with its front claws (this it manages to do within a matter of seconds), it probes with its tongue, sticky with saliva, for insects, their grubs and eggs.

AARDWOLF

Proteles cristatus

Many animals use deceit to protect themselves against their enemies, among them some that pretend to be much bigger, stronger and fiercer than they really are.

First prize in the false-size stakes must surely go to the harmless aardwolf. When threatened or otherwise under stress this shy little creature, just eight kilograms in weight, puffs out the long hairs of its mane to increase its bulk, indeed to resemble the fearsome, 60-kilogram spotted hyaena, whose distinct facial features it shares. It also utters a low-pitched, menacing growl quite at odds with its true, gentle nature (though it can be aggressive in defence of its territory).

The largely nocturnal aardwolf (which is related to the hyaena) is a highly specialized species, particularly when it comes to feeding: it lives almost entirely on harvester termites, or 'white ants', particularly of the *Trinervitermes* variety.

The latter are among the few types of termite that forage at night and also in the open veld. The aardwolf,

A

Luckily, though, it is also during these cool periods that other termites, the *Hodotermes*, emerge to offer an alternative food source, albeit one that is far less nutritious. The hard outer covering of the *Hodotermes* workers is pigmented enough to withstand direct sunlight, and they usually forage in the early mornings and late afternoons.

with its long wide tongue, broad palate and a stomach adapted to digest huge quantities of the termites' chemical secretions – poisons used as defence against predators – will consume up to 300 000 of the insects in a single night.

But specialization has its drawbacks. Unlike such insect-eaters as the aardvark and pangolin, which are expert diggers able to break open the hard termite mounds, aardwolves are physically weak and must forage on the surface of the veld. And, on cold winter nights, the *Trinervitermes* quite sensibly stay underground. At these times the aardwolf struggles, and many of the cubs die of starvation.

> The aardwolf can consume up to 300 000 termites in a single feeding session.

ADDERS
Family Viperidae

Also known as vipers, these reptiles are among the African continent's most poisonous snakes.

Best known southern African member of the family is probably the puff adder (*Bitis arietans*), whose venom is cytotoxic (it destroys the body's cells), the long, up to 18-millimetre fangs sinking deep into the flesh and causing gross swelling, extreme pain and necrosis (the destruction of tissue). The bites are always serious, although, surprisingly, relatively few prove fatal. Those deaths that do occur usually result from kidney failure and other complications arising from the swelling. The snake gets its common name from the way it puffs itself up when disturbed.

Largest of the family is the gaboon adder (*Bitis gabonica*), which can grow to a length of nearly two metres. It has an attractively patterned yellow, purple and brown body – colours which serve as superb camouflage on the leaf-littered forest floor of its habitat – and a distinctively flattened, triangular head. It too has huge fangs, its strike is lightning fast, and it can kill a human if it injects its full load of poison (which can be as much as 100 milligrams). However, its usual quarries are small rodents, ground-living birds, frogs and toads.

Other family members include the night adders, which lay eggs, and six other species of the genus *Bitis*, which give birth to live young. Among the latter are the mountain adders, and the horned adders, which for the most part live in the dry western areas (the famous sidewinder belongs to the genus) and, typically, bury themselves in the sand so that only the top of the head, the eyes and tip of the tail are visible. There they wait in ambush for passing prey. The sand also protects them from the often ferocious daytime heat and the night chill.

> *Largest of the viper family is the gaboon adder, which can grow to a length of nearly two metres.*

ALBATROSSES
Family Diomedeidae

These are among the largest of all flying birds (others are the marabou stork, the kori bustard and the Andean condor of South America). The wandering albatross (*Diomedea exulans*) boasts an especially magnificent wingspan: it usually reaches a full three metres from tip to tip; largest on record is 3,63 metres.

Eight species of these stately birds, which are related to the petrels, can be seen in southern African waters, gliding masterfully above the waves with scarcely a movement of their great wings, using the air currents for lift and their heads and tails as rudders. They rarely come within sight of the seaboard, heading for shore only when nesting or when a storm blows up.

Albatrosses stay out to sea for months on end, sleeping on the water, drinking seawater (they have their own built-in desalinization plants) and feeding on fish and squid captured at the surface. They also follow the trawler fleets, feasting on the discarded offal.

The bird's ability to glide for immense distances has prompted the myth that it sleeps on the wing. Legend also has it that should a sailor shoot an albatross, disaster will befall ship and crew – a seagoing belief that inspired Samuel Coleridge's famous *Rime of the Ancient Mariner*.

A

ANT LIONS
Family Myrmeleontidae

The young of some species of these insects, which look rather like dragon-flies, feed themselves in an especially ingenious way – by building traps for their prey.

The ant lion larva moves backwards, in circular fashion, beneath the surface of the soft ground, digging and flicking the earth away with jerks of its head. Soon enough it has created a funnel-shaped pit, at the bottom of which it lies, hidden by a layer of soil, waiting for a passing ant or other unsuspecting insect to stumble and fall in. Once over the edge, the victim struggles to escape up the crumbling sides of the pit. The larva makes its task even more difficult by flicking sand at the unwitting intruder.

Once within reach of the larva's powerful, curved mandibles, or jaws, the prey is seized. The ant lion does not chew and swallow the insect (it has no mouth) but, instead, sucks it dry of its vital juices.

ARCTIC TERN
Sterna paradisaea

These slender, elegant seabirds are among the best-travelled members of the natural world: when autumn comes to the northern hemisphere, they leave their breeding grounds in the Arctic wastelands to migrate across the equator and down to the southern seas – a distance of up to 20 000 kilometres. Some of the birds end their journey off the South African coast; most go on to the Antarctic islands, drawn by the abundant stocks of fish in the nutrient-rich waters, leaving again in March or April for the long flight back. During its 15-odd year lifespan a single tern will complete more than a million kilometres.

Travellers supreme

Other bird species are just as intrepid, perhaps even more so. The curlew sandpiper, seen throughout the subcontinent but in especially huge concentrations (up to 30 000 individuals) around Langebaan lagoon, on South Africa's south-western coast, is a summer visitor from the wastelands of the Siberian tundra. It takes the shortest route south – across central Russia and the Middle East and down along Africa's east coast. The lagoon's sanderlings and knots, on the other hand, choose a different route, around West Africa. All come to Langebaan for the incredibly bountiful food resources – molluscs, crustaceans and other minute organisms – of its waters, marshes and mudbanks. Experts estimate that each cubic centimetre of Langebaan mud contains up to 60 million bacteria – a rich soup indeed.

Other remarkable migrants from the north are the European swifts, some of whom begin their non-stop, 10 000-kilometre flight as fledgelings, remaining in the air even after they reach their southern African destinations: they eat and sleep on the wing until it's time to return to their far-off European and Asian breeding grounds.

The mysteries of migration

These and many other birds are endowed with a number of navigational aids, sensory abilities that enable them to find their way with almost uncanny accuracy to their far-off destinations.

Many if not all migrants have a built-in compass that charts the earth's magnetic field – lines of magnetic force whose angles change as the travellers fly high above land and sea. They can also calculate direction by the position of the sun and, at night, by the stars (the Pole Star is a constant reference in the northern hemisphere). Even heavy cloud cover poses few problems: the birds can still discern the general direction, the pattern of light filtering through and therefore the position of the sun. Many insects also use this 'polarized light' to determine their course.

ARGENTINE ANT
Iridomyrmex humilis

This tiny, exotic creature has wreaked havoc among local (especially Cape) plant populations since it first appeared on the scene a century ago. It continues to do so.

The Argentine ant arrived in cargoes of South American fodder destined for the horses of the British army during the Anglo-Boer war (1899–1902), and happily went forth to multiply. Today, the accidental invasion threatens more than half of South Africa's 331 species of protea.

These aggressive intruders have progressively displaced indigenous ants and thus disrupted the delicate process by means of which the latter distribute and 'plant' the protea's seeds. As a result, such wild flowers as the lovely blushing bride and marsh rose could disappear forever. The ants have also attacked colonies of bees, and given protection to scale insects and other pests that plague the Western Cape's beautiful vineyards and orchards.

A

BABOON

Papio cynocephalus ursinus

Baboons travel across the open veld in a kind of 'battle formation', with the females and youngsters in the middle.

Watch a troop of baboons for a while and you'll be amazed at the number of different ways in which its members relate to and react with one another. At any given moment some are happy in their own company, others gather in cliques; some are playing, others fighting, still others grooming each other. In any baboon community you'll find pretty well the full range of what we regard as virtues and vices: courage, strength, natural leadership; greed, envy, deceitfulness – they're all there. In short, each animal has its own, very distinctive personality.

But one quality, an intensely sociable nature, is common to all. This, plus its varied diet, its opportunism, its intelligence and the ability to adapt to most conditions, makes the baboon a fascinating subject of study in the context of humankind's own distant origins.

The chacma baboon is a large primate (fourth biggest in Africa after the gorilla, chimpanzee and bonobo) with a long, dog-like face, powerful shoulders, long canine teeth (in the male), and bare buttocks with patches of thickened skin which, in females, swell and turn red according to the phases of the sexual cycle.

It is a remarkably agile and sometimes aggressive animal that spends its days moving in a troop (which can be more than 100 strong but averages around 40 members) across the veld in search of the wild fruits, bulbs, roots, scorpions, insects and other small items it feeds on. When it gets the chance it will also catch and eat vertebrate prey such as birds, hares and even young antelope.

Family, friend and foe

Baboon society reflects the ultimate in chauvinism: all adult males (those five years of age or older) are dominant over all females. But within that broad arrangement there is an

elaborate and ever-changing network of personal relationships. Friendship is the cement that holds a baboon troop together, and is expressed by its members grooming each other (searching the fur and skin for foreign particles and parasites such as ticks) – behaviour that establishes an intricate, subtly defined network of individual alliances and rivalries. Within each troop are smaller birth groups of females – daughters, sisters, cousins, aunts – who cluster around and recognize the authority of the oldest member. These females maintain a lifelong loyalty to their extended family, but often mix with and indeed form close friendships with females from other groups.

These close-knit communities accept male members, but entry isn't an automatic or even a simple process: the newcomer must charm his way into the group, prove to them that he's a trustworthy friend. This he does gradually and with infinite patience, making his first overtures to just one female, gaining her confidence, grooming her, and then going on to cultivate other females until, eventually, he is allowed to copulate with one or more of them.

Only dominant males, however, are allowed to mate with females that are receptive (in oestrus).

A pregnant female or one who has given birth (the gestation period is around 140 days; she produces a single offspring roughly once every two years) forms special relationships with up to three of the troop's males. The guardians stay close to the mother at all times, and will often defend her when there's trouble.

The baboon group

The troop is led by a large and thoroughly bossy male, a supremo who decides where and when to move, whether to run away from a threat (always the preferred option) or to stand and fight. It's a popular but mistaken belief that baboons post sentries when they are out and about or, come sundown, when they retire to sleep. The myth derives from the animal's inquisitive nature: individuals will often climb a rock or tree to survey their surroundings simply because they want to know what's going on, and of course they will sound the alarm if they spot something unusual or threatening.

However, baboons do travel across open terrain in a kind of 'battle formation', with the female baboons and youngsters in the middle, the tougher males to either side, the lower ranks at the front and rear.

If they are forced to confront a predator – a leopard that suddenly pounces from a tree or rocky outcrop, for example (though this is less common than supposed) – the baboons will give a very good account of themselves. They grimace, caper and scream, the males wildly waving their arms and baring their lethal fangs, and it takes a brave intruder indeed to accept the challenge.

B

Helping hands

Baboons and other primates are sometimes called on to prove themselves in the workplace. In Malaysia, little maquaque monkeys harvest coconuts from lofty palm trees and one (in Australia) is 'employed' to drive his owner's tractor. Even more remarkably, some South American capuchin monkeys have been trained to help disabled people around the house, washing, feeding and even preparing drinks for their charges. Perhaps southern Africa's most notable such 'employee' was Jack, a chacma baboon whose owner, a railway guard named James Wide, had lost his legs in an accident and was posted to Uitenhage as a signalman. Wide trained Jack to work the signal levers and act as general helper, for which he was paid a 'salary' of rations and the occasional half-bottle of brandy.

BAG-WORM MOTHS

Family Psychidae

These insects, of which there are more than a hundred species in southern Africa, are noted for the way their larvae build little houses, or bags, for themselves from silk, twigs, bark, leaves and bits of grass or grit. These they live in permanently, carrying the structure around with them (the home has a single entrance, from which the head protrudes) when they move from place to place. Each species has its own architectural style – the wattle bag-worm, for example, 'thatches' its house with slivers of dry bark and leaves.

Even more extraordinary is the female's life cycle. She never develops wings, and remains in her house during the pupating stage, and even after she's reached full maturity, attaching the structure firmly to a tree and awaiting the arrival of a winged male. Following fertilization she lays her eggs and then, still in her bag, gradually shrivels until her entire body is a mass of eggs. All that's left of her is the head and a bit of flaky skin.

When the eggs hatch (in August), the young larva emerges, descends on a strand of silk and waits for the breeze to blow it away onto a nutritious leaf. If it isn't happy with its new resting place, it will simply repeat the process. Sometimes, in a good wind, it will be blown several kilometres (a method of transport known as 'ballooning') – perhaps into cultivated lands, which can be devastated by the infestations.

The power of two

Male and female moths have an uncanny ability to find each other, sometimes across quite unbelievable distances. The secret: a powerful substance called pheromone, produced by the female in tiny quantities but so strongly scented that males can detect its presence, and the direction of the source, over several kilometres. So minute are the quantities of the female's pheromone that, in one experiment, the output of a million moths were collected to produce a store of just 12 milligrams. And so sensitive are the male's antennae (they are covered in more than 50 000 microscopic hairs, most of them designed to detect this one chemical) that he can identify and react to a single molecule.

Pheromones are not specific to moths: they provide the sexual trigger for many insects, for rodents, and for mammals – including primates, though whether or not they play a prominent part in human sexual response is still inconclusive.

These trees grow to an immense size, their girths reaching 20 metres and more in circumference. And to a great age: it is reckoned that a specimen with a diameter of more than ten metres is probably over 3 000 years old. One huge, hollowed out baobab near the town of Leydsdorp, in South Africa's Northern Province, even served as a bar-room for the thirsty diggers of the Murchison gold rush in the 1880s (unhappily, it is no longer standing).

Baobabs bear large, white, scented flowers that are pollinated by bats. These open out just before the sun sets, last for just 24 hours, and produce egg-shaped fruits that some animals find quite delicious. The trees are also useful to man.

BAOBAB TREE
Adansonia digitata

There are many legends surrounding these grotesque giants of the hot African plains. And quite understandably so for, with their thick grey trunks and spindly branches they really do look extraordinary. Some rural folk believe that God planted them upside down, or that they simply fell from heaven to plunge head first into the ground; that their blossoms are haunted by spirits; that a drink made from the seeds will protect you from crocodile attacks.

B

The fruits have a white pulp containing, among other things, tartaric acid, ascorbic acid (vitamin C) and potassium bitartrate (also known as 'cream of tartar') which, when mixed with water, makes a refreshing drink; the leaves can be boiled and eaten as a vegetable, the seeds roasted and ground to produce a fairly palatable coffee-like beverage; ash from the burnt wood serves as a substitute for table salt. The hollows and cavities among the branches capture and retain rainwater – a boon to villagers and to early travellers in times of severe drought.

Appearances, though, are deceptive, for this solid-looking tree is in fact little more than a mass of soft fibrous wood and water, and though it may have started life before the birth of the Roman empire, enduring everything the centuries could throw at it, its death is sudden, swift and complete. Disease may kill it, or it could collapse because its bole has absorbed too much rainwater, and it will simply crumble in on itself to become a barely noticeable pile of flaky vegetable matter – a sad ending to one of the kings of the plant world.

The fox's ears are used as super-sensitive amplifiers to pinpoint its underground prey.

BAT-EARED FOX

Otocyon megalotis

Few of Africa's mammals are as enchanting as this little animal, with its bushy black tail, rounded back, pointed muzzle and, its most eye-catching feature, its improbably large, dish-like ears.

These appendages are perfectly adapted to the fox's lifestyle: they are used as super-sensitive sound amplifiers to pinpoint the exact position of the harvester termites and beetle larvae that make up its favourite food. The ears are held forward as it listens for the faint sounds of its prey beneath the ground, and the insects stand little chance of avoiding detection, even at night. It also eats a fair selection of other creatures, including scorpions, spiders, rodents, locusts, and certain plants.

The fox has other unusual qualities. It is a monogamous species, staying 'married' to its mate for its entire adult life. Parenting duties are shared; the mother provides much of the food for the offspring while, for much of the time, the father guards the den and its young occupants.

BATELEUR

Terathopius ecaudatus

Bateleur is the French word for acrobat or juggler, and conjures up the perfect image – the bird, an eagle, shows a quite superb control of the air as it rolls, tumbles and somersaults in its spectacular display flight.

This is perhaps the most striking of southern Africa's birds of prey, splendid in its finery, instantly recognizable by its velvet-black head and breast, chestnut back, red legs, feet and beak surrounds (the cere), and by its ridiculously short, stumpy tail.

The tail looks incongruous, giving its owner a squat, awkward appearance when at rest. But in flight the bird is poetry in motion, a showcase of delta-winged elegance as it planes along, usually at low altitude, on its arrow-straight course, its only bodily movement a gentle canting from side to side. Indeed the original meaning of the French name was 'tightrope walker', which is also highly descriptive of these magnificent birds.

Bateleurs have superb eyesight (though not as good as the vulture's), able to pinpoint their prey – small mammals, ground-living birds, reptiles and, especially, carcasses — from an astonishing distance. But the preference for carrion largely explains the bird's disappearance from much of southern Africa: it has been virtually exterminated by poison bait put out by stockfarmers to keep marauders such as jackals away from their cattle and sheep. The crafty jackal has survived well enough, though, while eagles and other harmless, incidental creatures have been brought to the edge of extinction.

BATS

Order Chiroptera

Many of these flying mammals have amazing abilities to find their way in the dark, and to hunt the insects they eat, by sound – a phenomenon known as 'echolocation'.

To do so they send out rapid sequences of high-pitched clicks, bleeps and shrieks whose sound waves bounce off objects (including the bodies of insects). These sounds may comprise up to a phenomenal 230 000 vibrations each second – far above a human's audible range, whose upper limit is about 18 000 vibrations a second. The bat listens for the echoes with its large ears, and so sensitive is its hearing that it can immediately estimate the direction and distance of the quarry.

B

The target is usually a moth – easy prey, one would think, because it is smaller, slower, less able to manœuvre than its hunter.

But moths have evolved their own defence mechanisms: they have rudimentary ears (unusual in insects) and can hear the bat's shrieks, even calculate more or less the direction the animal is coming from and its approximate distance.

Moreover, the moth usually has time to take evasive action, indeed to pre-empt the attack: it can hear the bat before being detected itself, and will take off on a looping escape flight. Some species – tiger moths, for example – have a second line of defence, producing a sharp little sound just before contact in order to startle the attacker, so putting it off its stride. It may also fold its wings and plunge to earth, where it becomes undetectable against the solid background.

The two sub-orders of bats are the Megachiroptera, or fruit-eating species (though they also feed on other vegetable matter) and once commonly known as 'flying foxes'; and the insect-eating (and in some cases carnivorous) Microchiroptera. Among the latter are the horseshoe bats, a family named for the curious shield-like feature on the front of the face; the somewhat similar trident and leaf-nosed bats; the common slit-faced bats (skin-folds on the face cover sensitive echolocation organs); vesper bats (seen flying high on clear-skied nights); free-tailed bats (which have faces rather like that of a bulldog), and sheath-tailed bats, which include the tomb bats. The latter hang in pairs against a vertical surface and will move away in crablike fashion when disturbed.

BEE-EATERS
Family Meropidae

These are the most colourful of all our birds, each individual jewel-like in its brilliant plumage. They are also among the more accomplished of nature's engineers.

Some species, like the carmine bee-eater, are colonial breeders, nesting in their thousands in the tunnels they excavate along the river-banks to create a dazzling symphony in scarlet and dark blue. In some areas the banks are riddled with openings, the whole looking rather like a vast tenement block.

Once a carmine bee-eater has found its partner, the pair will select a suitable spot and begin digging a metre-long tunnel that slopes upwards, hollowing out a nest chamber at the inner end and building an earth barrier at the entrance to prevent the eggs rolling out.

The nest is safe enough deep in the earth, but hygiene tends to be sacrificed to security. Droppings and food waste often accumulate rapidly; insects move in and deposit their larvae, and the tunnel soon becomes almost unbearably fouled.

Eight bee-eater species occur in southern Africa. All have the long, slender, slightly curved bills of the insect-eater but otherwise differ markedly in size and colour. Among the most attractive are the white-fronted bee-eater (crimson and pink throat, white crown, green wings and tail feathers) and the European bee-eater (yellow throat, pale blue under-feathers, chestnut crown and back).

BILHARZIA WORMS

Schistosoma species

The life cycle of these minute organisms ranks among the most complex of all creatures. To survive, the worm needs three entirely different elements: water, a snail, and a mammal (preferably human) body – and in the process of surviving it will transmit bilharzia, a debilitating, often dangerous and sometimes fatal disease.

After developing its larval stage in a water snail, the bilharzia fluke seeks out and penetrates the skin of a person entering the water, and thence travels via the veins or lymph system

To survive, the worm needs three elements: water, a snail, and a mammal.

through the heart and lungs to lodge in the liver, where it grows into an adult worm, mates and moves on to the bladder, kidneys, intestine or other parts of the body. There the worms lay their eggs, which then leave the body in the waste products. The eggs will only hatch, however, if they are discharged into fresh water, where the hatchlings swim around until they find another snail host – and so the cycle begins all over again.

Bilharzia (or schistosomiasis) is sometimes difficult to diagnose because the symptoms can be vague. Usually, though, a rash appears a couple of days after contact with infected water, followed in a few weeks by fever and muscular pain. Much later – perhaps months, perhaps even years – the victim will suffer bouts of abdominal pain, diarrhoea, and a burning sensation when discharging urine, in which there may be blood.

Once diagnosed, the disease responds well to drugs. There is, however, no vaccination against bilharzia: one simply has to avoid rivers and dams in bilharzia-prone areas. These include parts of the Eastern Cape, KwaZulu-Natal and the northern regions of the subcontinent.

B

BLACK-BACKED JACKAL

Canis mesomelas

Probably the most versatile of all southern Africa's animals, the jackal both hunts and scavenges, mainly at night but also during the daylight hours, and will eat just about anything that moves and much that doesn't. It is able to live in almost any kind of African environment except forest country, from the desert regions (it generally prefers dry terrain) to the wettest of areas – those receiving more than 2 000 millimetres of rainfall a year.

Depending on the opportunities, it will take young antelope, small mammals such as springhares (or, more correctly, springhaas), rodents, snakes and lizards, locusts, termites and other insects, birds' eggs and fledgelings, carrion, and wild fruits and berries. Sometimes it hunts and forages on its own, sometimes in pairs; occasionally – in tough times, for example, when the antelope are dying of starvation – it comes together in groups of 20 or 30 individuals to demolish a carcass. In fact these attractive little creatures (they grow up to 12 kilograms in weight) are tenacious thieves, showing great bravery at kills made by the larger carnivores. They will nip at the heels of lions and spotted hyaenas, hurrying their bigger, more dangerous rivals along in order to gain access to the carcass that much sooner.

Jackals will even take part at kills-in-the-making: they have been seen following a cheetah as it stalks an antelope herd. Sometimes, when they are out hunting springbok or impala, for instance, one member of the pack will distract the mother while the others isolate and bring down her calf. They are also able to pick out the old and the weak from a herd, and in doing so they play a significant role in maintaining the balance in, and the health of, the ecosystem.

BONTEBOK

Damaliscus pygargus

This rather lovely animal, with its white, black and rich brown markings, its white face-blaze and rump and its elegant horns, is perhaps southern Africa's rarest antelope. Indeed, it could very easily have become extinct – and therein lies a story with a happy ending.

The bontebok once roamed the southern plains in great numbers, but the early white colonists hunted the animal so enthusiastically that by the early 1830s just a few, a barely viable population, remained to propagate the species. In that decade, though, a group of Cape farmers decided to keep the surviving herds in safety on their lands – a piece of foresight rare in an era when 'conservation' meant practically nothing.

Nevertheless their numbers continued to decline, so that a century later not more than 30 specimens were known to have survived. So in 1931 the animals – a breeding herd of just 17 – were given asylum within the newly established Bontebok National Park, in the southwestern Cape region.

The result: an eventual but clear victory for the conservationists. Today the park holds between 200 and 300 bontebok; a further 400 (the largest single herd) have found a home in the nearby De Hoop reserve, and there are over 1 000 more scattered among various game farms and other protected areas.

BUCHU
Agathosma species

Among the most useful (to humans) of all plants are two species of the buchu shrub, *Agathosma crenulata* and *A. betulina*, which are members of the citrus family. Both grow naturally in the Western Cape, and have long been a part of the culture of the Khoisan peoples. It also became a popular health aid among the early Dutch colonists at the Cape, and indeed is still widely used as a household medicine.

Buchu leaves yield valuable essential oils, which among other things act as a diuretic and a cure for hangovers (the oil once enjoyed wide sales in Europe and North America). It is also used to make a soothing beverage and as a remedy for kidney and urinary tract diseases.

B

Strained and sore muscles have traditionally been treated with buchu vinegar, and buchu 'brandy' – the leaves are steeped in an alcoholic brew – is recommended for a range of stomach and flu-type ailments. These the potion may not cure, but it certainly helps relieve the discomfort, if only temporarily.

BUFFALO
Syncerus caffer

For hunters, this large animal – Africa's only species of wild cattle and a relative of the antelopes – is among the most dangerous of quarries. Solitary males, perhaps thrown out of the herd after losing a mating battle, can be very aggressive, cunning and unpredictable: if wounded, they will back-track, hide in ambush until their pursuer comes within range, and then attack without warning. Lone bulls are often seen close to streams and waterholes.

This is a large (up to 800-kilogram) and immensely powerful animal, one of the famed 'big five' so sought after by game-viewers. It is easily distinguished by its bulk, its massive, upward curving horns and by the heavy, bony boss on its forehead. It feeds mainly on grasses, mostly during the cooler parts of the day, seeking shade in the bush during the hot hours. Buffalo are good swimmers, and can often be seen wallowing in muddy pools. When a herd is threatened, the animals will usually come together in a circle, facing outwards to form a kind of defensive 'laager'.

BUSHBABIES
Family Lorisidae

These endearing little nocturnal forest-living primates, of which there are three species in the southern African region, are famous for the remarkable way they can leap from tree to tree and branch to branch. Indeed the South African lesser bushbaby (*Galago moholi*) can clear a full five metres – that is, around 33 times the length of its own body!

The common English name, though appropriate to the appearance of these small, gentle, wide-eyed, furry, entirely lovable creatures, is actually derived from

the cries of the thick-tailed bushbaby (*Otolemur crassicaudatus*), which are loud and uncannily like those of a distressed human infant.

In fact this is only one of 18 different sounds it makes, each serving a particular purpose – including raucous shrieks to attract others of its kind or to intimidate strangers: frenzied squawks, whistles and cackles when alarmed, and a soft buzzing the youngsters give out when separated from their mother.

The lesser bushbaby has an even wider repertoire, which embraces 24 calls, often running into one another or mixed together to produce a complex 'language'. It can also utter a call when breathing in (as well as when exhaling), which sometimes leads the listener to think the sounds are being made by two animals.

> *The bushbaby can leap a full five metres – that is, around 33 times the length of its own body.*

Bushbabies spend nearly all their time in trees (but will sometimes take to the ground, where they will hop along on their two hindlimbs), feeding on insects and gum. The thick-tailed species also eats wild fruit; Grant's bushbaby (*Galagoides granti*), which is confined to a small region of eastern Mozambique and to parts of Zimbabwe, eats little or no gum, preying mainly on insects and other invertebrates.

BUTTERFLIES
Order Lepidoptera

The most common of all the subcontinent's butterflies is the painted lady (*Vanessa cardui*), an orange-brown insect that one often sees

flying in huge numbers, and for great distances, when migrating. It is also the most cosmopolitan of all, occurring in every part of the world except South America and Australasia.

Southern Africa is home to more than 850 different butterfly species, the most primitive of which are the little brown and grey skippers (family Hesperiidae), which have an erratic and darting flight.

Other prominent families include the so-called whites (Pieridae), though some are yellow and others beautifully marked with orange, purple and red blotches; the blues and coppers (Lycaenidae), some of which are rare and much sought after by collectors; the swallowtails and swordtails (Papilionidae), among which is the emperor swallowtail, the

B

largest of all the region's species, with a wingspan, in the females, of up to 120 millimetres; and the snout butterfly, which has a whole family (Libytheidae) all to itself.

Arguably the most fascinating are the Nymphalidae, which embraces subfamilies commonly termed monarchs, reds, browns, nymphs, commodores and charaxes (or swifts). Some species are quite superb mimics; many are highly unpalatable to predators: the monarchs, for instance, lay their eggs on the leaves of the poisonous milkweed plant, the caterpillars absorbing and storing the toxin and keeping it even when they turn into butterflies. Their strident colours act as warnings to birds on the hunt for tasty morsels.

Although butterflies and moths are similar, they can be readily distinguished: the former are daytime creatures, have club-tipped feelers and rest with their wings closed against each other. More than 10 000 different moth species occur in southern Africa and at their larval stage, as caterpillars, they can cause a great deal of damage in both town and country. Among the more destructive are the clothes moths, which are especially partial to wool; the cabbage or diamond-backed moth, which infests cabbage plants; and the apple codling moth, an alien species which can devastate whole orchards.

BUTTON SPIDER
Latrodectus species

This is one of the two most venemous of all southern African spiders (the other is the genus *Sicarius*: see Spiders, page 100). The female of the species – more properly known as the black button spider and, in America, as the black widow – is the one to keep clear of: it is by far the larger and more dangerous of the two sexes, its venom attacking the nervous system and very occasionally (in about five percent of untreated cases) causing death in humans.

The spider (the female, that is) is easily recognizable. It is medium sized (10 to 15 millimetres) with an almost perfectly round, dark-brown or pitch-black, velvety body with a red mark or marks just above the spinnerets. The male is tiny (three millimetres) and insignificant.

The black button spider is a creature of the veld and of the farmlands, notably the Western Cape's wheat belt, but can also be found in built-up areas. It constructs its nest, on or just above the ground, in many and various places: under bushes, on tufts of grass and under logs. More common in suburban gardens is the brown button spider, found among shrubs, under discarded bricks and other backyard bits and pieces, along the base of a wall and even inside the house. It has a red hour-glass pattern on the front of its abdomen and its bite, though much less severe than that of its black cousin, merits close medical attention.

It will only bite you if you touch it accidentally, pressing it against your skin, and even then you'll barely notice. But a few minutes later the symptoms begin to appear: dizziness, painful stomach cramps, sweating, nausea, possibly a loss of consciousness. Just how bad these symptoms are, of course, depends on the amount of poison absorbed into the bloodstream; in most cases they're fairly mild. Either way, seek treatment straightaway: the antivenom is highly effective.

CAMELTHORN TREE

Acacia erioloba

This handsome and hardy resident of southern Africa's drier areas, like many desert plants (see page 36), has evolved an elaborate and ingenious way of propagating: it relies on the digestive systems of larger animals.

The tree produces surprisingly few seeds, but the pods are big, full of nutritious protein and most attractive to gemsbok, eland and other antelope – and the contents are well protected. Each pod is covered in a hard 'tunic' which acts as a protective, watertight casing containing seeds with extremely hard walls which are also more-or-less impervious to water. This enables the pod to remain on the ground for long periods. Gemsbok and eland are extremely fond of the pods and often swallow them whole. The casing and seedcoats are softened by the animal's digestive acids and, once the seeds pass out in the faeces, they are further softened by moisture and germinate with the first rains. Moreover, the seeds are usually passed out in a place favourable to growth because the animal and parent tree share the same habitat. And growth prospects are improved even further by the nutrient-rich dung in which the seeds are deposited.

The relationship between plants and browsing animals is – as with nearly every association in the wild – superbly designed to benefit both parties.

As in just about every association between different species, the relationship between plants and browsing animals is superbly designed to benefit both parties. The browsers get their food, and in return scatter the seeds over a wide area.

B

CAPE FLORISTIC KINGDOM

This botanical region is one of the world's great natural wonders: it covers less than one fiftieth of one percent of the earth's land area, yet so rich is it in plant families, genera and species that it is classed as one of only six floristic kingdoms, enjoying equal status with the immense Boreal (Holarctic) Kingdom that stretches over North America and most of Europe and Asia.

The region, which covers the largely winter rainfall areas (including the Cape Fold mountains) along the subcontinent's south-western and southern coastal belt, is home to around 8 600 different plant species – more than in the whole of the United Kingdom, and more than half the number in Australia, which is almost 100 times greater in extent. As many as 120 species have been found growing in a patch the size of the average middle-class suburban garden; of the 989 genera, fully 193 can be represented in a particular area.

For the most part this floral richness, associated mainly with a vegetation type known as 'fynbos' ('fine bush'), comprises hardy, low growing, evergreen, small-leaved shrubs such as proteas, ericas, the leafless, reed-like restios and many bulbous and cormous plants.

The species are mainly of ancient origin, well adapted to nutrient-poor soils, summer droughts and high winds – conditions introduced when the Cape's climate underwent radical change some 12 million years ago. Since then they have managed to withstand other, lesser, climatic upheavals partly by 'migrating' between the many refuges provided by the Cape mountains.

As with so much of southern Africa's natural heritage, many fynbos species are under threat. Among its chief enemies are alien vegetation (notably Australian wattles), too-frequent fires, pollution, encroachment of farmlands and urban sprawl, and the picked-flower industry.

CAPE PENDULINE TIT
Anthoscopus minutus

This charming, lively, plumpish little olive-grey and yellow songbird has evolved an unusually crafty way of protecting its eggs: it fashions a false entrance to its nest. This is a fairly prominent hole at the top, easily seen but leading nowhere – it simply ends in a cul-de-sac.

The real entrance is close by and all but invisible, a minute slit that the bird prises open with its foot in order to pass through, and which automatically springs back into the closed position after its passage.

The nest as a whole is also a special affair, especially that constructed by the Cape bird's European cousin.

The male, who is the builder, starts building the nest by tying a single, sturdy strand of grass or animal hair to a twig (he does this with his expert beak); making a frame from the rest of the strand and then weaving in more strands to create a tough little hanging basket (hence 'penduline'). He then knots shorter bits of plant material into the structure to give it even more strength.

The bird's mate adds the more feminine comforts of home to the nest, lining the interior with soft plant material.

When he is satisfied with his work, he advertises for and recruits a mate, who adds the more feminine comforts of home to the nest, lining its interior with soft plant material. She then lays her clutch of up to six eggs. So tough and neat are the nests that, in East Africa, they are used as purses by some country women. Apparently, too, children in certain parts of rural eastern Europe wear them as slippers.

The origin of the curious word 'tit' is uncertain, but it seems to be derived from the Icelandic 'tittr', which means 'pin'. The full English name is 'titmouse'.

CARACAL
Caracal caracal

Few of Africa's animals can match this handsome, medium-sized cat for agility and fierceness. So quick are its responses that it is able to catch a bird on the wing, its immensely powerful hindlegs propelling it metres high to pluck its startled quarry from the air.

The caracal's main prey, however, comprises rodents and the smaller antelope, which it stalks to within a few metres and then pounces with lightning speed. And it will protect its kill with vigour. Indeed it is the very embodiment of fury as it spits and hisses defiance at the jackals that hover at mealtimes. It is also fearless, and extremely dangerous, when wounded or cornered, quite able and more than willing to attack a human intruder.

The cat, a creature of the more open savanna regions (it also occurs in Arabia, the Near East and India), is distinguished by its reddish brown colouring, its pointed and tufted ears and its luminous amber eyes.

C

Caracals, which have few natural enemies, are renowned poultry and stock thieves, and are consequently disliked and persecuted by farmers. In southern Africa the species is also known as the rooikat (which means 'red cat' in Afrikaans) – and as the lynx, though it is an entirely different animal from its European and North American namesake.

CHAMELEONS
Family Chamaeleonidae

These arboreal lizards look for all the world like fierce little monsters when threatened, puffing themselves up prodigiously, hissing their fury through wide-gaping mouths. Indeed their name is derived from the Greek for 'dwarf lion'.

In reality, though, chameleons are wholly innocuous: weak of tooth and claw, painfully slow-moving, and highly vulnerable to a bustling shrike or swooping bird of prey as they creep, centimetre by centimetre, along an exposed tree-branch.

They do, though, have two effective weapons in their defensive armoury. First, they can change their body colour, from pale pink right across the spectrum to near-black, to blend almost perfectly (and safely) into their environment. Second, they are able to swivel their eyes independently, using them both to locate the insects they feed on (though the eyes are sharply focused for the purpose of capturing them) and to keep a caulious look-out for predators.

Chameleons live on insects and arachnids: beetles and grasshoppers, spiders, centipedes and suchlike, hunting their prey by stealth. They move with great deliberation until they spot one of these creatures at rest, bring their two eyes to bare, mark the spot, inch forward until they're within range, and then shoot out their long, sticky tongues (which can be almost the length of their bodies) to haul in their victims. During all this they maintain balance by grasping a twig with their prehensile tails and remarkably efficient fingers and toes.

Two genera of chameleons are found in the southern African region. The *Bradypodion* ('slow foot') are dwarf species that produce live young, up to ten in number, which can function well on their own within minutes of birth. Much larger are the two species of Chamaeleo, which lay eggs. The flap-necked chameleon (*Chamaeleo dilepsis*) grows to a head-to-tail-tip length of around 35 centimetres. Biggest of the wider region's species is the giant *Chamaeleo oustaleti* of Madagascar, which can reach over half a metre in length.

Though they are quite harmless to man (and indeed can be most useful, helping to control insect pests), chameleons remain the undeserving objects of myth, superstition and fear in many parts of rural Africa.

CHEETAH
Acinonyx jubatus

During the brief, explosive hunt-and-kill sequence this graceful cat, swiftest of all the world's land animals, can attain 70 km/h within three seconds – an acceleration rate, from a standing start, comparable to that of a Grand Prix car – and at full throttle will cover the ground at around 100 km/h.

The cheetah is superbly built for speed: it has a sinuous, streamlined body, small head, deep keel-like chest, long and powerful legs and a long tail that helps maintain perfect balance during the zig-zag chase. It is also blessed with a remarkably supple spine, which it arches and then stretches, allowing it to take enormous strides. Its vision remains clear even during the drama of the chase: as it bounds across the veld, the head is held steady on flexible shoulders, and the light-sensitive cells of the eye's retina keep the target in focus.

The price of speed
But this high level of physical specialization has its downside. The cheetah has very little stamina: during the lightning-fast sprint its body temperature soars, a great deal of energy is released and the effort cannot be sustained for more than a few seconds. If the prey, usually a medium-sized antelope such as a springbok, isn't caught within 400 metres, 600 at most, the cat just gives up.

The cheetah's rate of acceleration can be compared to that of a racing car.

And after a successful chase it cannot eat straightaway: instead it must rest, exhausted and panting, for about 15 minutes – time enough for the vultures and other carnivorous scavengers to move in.

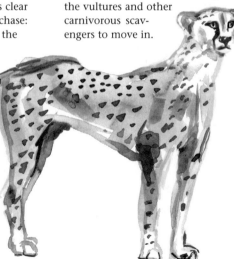

C

So the cheetah must get as close as possible, preferably within 50 metres, before launching itself at the quarry. Just how it does this depends on the conditions: sometimes the antelope appear entirely unconcerned about its presence (a curious phenomenum among herd animals) and it will simply edge its way forward. At other times, if there is good ground cover, it will stalk them.

Nor is the cheetah a robust creature. It does not have the brute strength of the other big cats, the lions and leopards. It also lacks their retractable claws, which puts it at a serious disadvantage in confrontations with better-armed competitors.

Other elements have also been sacrificed to speed. For example, it cannot rotate the wrists of its forelimbs – an adaptation that does help keep the animal steady during its first furious dash, but also prevents it from performing the acrobatic twisting and turning needed when its prey changes direction at the last moment. Moreover, the cat's relatively light frame – it weighs in at around 40 kilograms – its weak jaws, small teeth and essentially gentle nature render it curiously submissive to other meat-eaters, and it is often robbed of its prey by the bigger cats and by hyaenas.

The cheetah therefore minimizes the chances of conflict over food by hunting during the hot daylight hours, a time when other large carnivores are resting up in shady places.

Family life

Female cheetah live independent and solitary lives, their only company the latest litter of perhaps five or six cubs. The male is needed only for breeding purposes: the mother is quite capable of looking after her offspring without help, and in dry regions like the Kalahari desert she will cover a lot of ground in search of prey. Her home range overlaps with those of other cheetahs but she doesn't seem to place much importance on territorial rights: she tolerates intrusion, simply avoiding direct contact with her peers. At some point, usually about 18 months after their birth, the cubs will leave the family circle to wander the veld as a mixed-sex group. In due course the males pair up or get together in a threesome to hunt, to scent-mark and defend their turf.

In a curious piece of evolutionary trickery, a cheetah cub will grow a mane. The extra fur has several uses: it enables the mother to get a good grip as she carries her offspring; it may provide a degree of camouflage and, most intriguingly, it makes the youngster look bigger and fiercer, which helps keep predators at bay.

Survival of the species

The cheetah is an endangered species. Much of its traditional habitat, the open grassland plains, has been taken over by farm- and ranchlands. Moreover, the gene pool lacks diversity, which triggers sperm abnormalities that inhibit breeding and renders the animal vulnerable to disease. And those that do reach maturity are too delicate, physically, to compete confidently with the stronger carnivores.

Efforts are being made to breed cheetahs in captivity, notably at the De Wildt research centre near the Magaliesberg hills west of Pretoria. The experts were sceptical at first, but since its establishment in 1971 the centre has enjoyed huge success, producing more than 400 cubs. Pride of De Wildt is the king cheetah, an especially beautiful animal with a strikingly marked coat on which the typical cheetah's spots are enlarged, flowing into heavy black blotches and stripes. The king cheetah is not a separate species but a rare genetic variation that occasionally crops up in normal families.

COBRAS
Family Elapidae

Among the best known of these front-fanged, extremely poisonous snakes, famed for the distinctive 'hood' they display when they rear up to attack, is the banded or snouted cobra, a common resident of the bushveld areas of southern Africa and farther north to the Nile River valley.

The snouted cobra can grow to a length of 2,5 metres, is olive to brown in colour with, in some

The cobra's bite is often fatal: just over 10 percent of its store of venom can kill.

specimens, a series of yellow bands across body and tail. Like other cobras, its bite is often fatal (just over 10 per cent of its store of venom can kill a human), the poison attacking the body's nervous system and causing death through paralysis and respiratory failure.

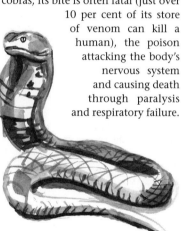

Smaller but just as deadly, if not more so, is the Cape cobra, which you can stumble across on Karoo farms and in other dry areas, and which is responsible for most of the fatal bites recorded in the Western and Northern Cape provinces of South Africa.

Then there's the forest cobra, which favours a watery and well-treed habitat and has an unusually

C

long lifespan (one captive specimen lived for nearly 30 years). This is a venomous snake, but rarely bites – mainly because it is usually too alert to be surprised.

None of these three spit their venom. By contrast, the Mozambique spitting cobra, the black-necked spitting cobra and the related rinkhals (not a 'true' cobra) may spray enough of their poison into the eyes of an intruder to cause blindness.

If its poison fails and it finds itself cornered, the rinkhals (and to a lesser degree the snouted cobra) will sham death, turning belly-up with its mouth wide open.

COELACANTH

Latimeria chalumnae

One day just before Christmas, 1938, trawlerman Captain N. Goosen netted an enormous, strange-looking mauve fish in the waters off East London. So sure was he of its rarity that he persuaded a taxi-driver to take it to Marjorie Courtenay-Latimer, director of the local museum. Days later the remains

(the carcass had been gutted and mounted) were identified by J.L.B. Smith, a professor at Rhodes University, as the coelacanth, a primitive species that flourished in the seas of the Mesozoic era some 250 million years ago and was thought to have been extinct for the past 70 million years and more. He described it as a 'living fossil'.

Coelacanths were among the very first fishes to have horny, overlapping scales and proper teeth, and unlike other inhabitants of the ocean they remained virtually unchanged in form for more than 200 million years. Many fossils had been found, indicating that they had once been present in great numbers.

At first the scientific world regarded Smith's specimen as a freak, a lone escapee from the deeper waters to which the last few, defeated coelacanths had been driven by competition from more advanced kinds of fish. Smith thought otherwise, sure in his own mind that it wasn't a degenerate species but a powerful predator that still lived in faraway parts of the western Indian Ocean. He could, he wrote, imagine ordinary fishing folk 'feasting on succulent coelacanth steaks on a remote Madagascan shore'. In the event he was proved right: a second specimen was caught off the Comoro Islands in 1952; another followed a year later, and several more have been captured over the years since then.

CORMORANTS
Family Phalacrocoracidae

Like other seabirds, these agile, long-necked, hook-billed birds, which dive deep in search of their fish prey, have evolved one especially useful feature: they are able to focus their eyes both above and below the surface of the water.

When it comes to eyesight, nearly every one of the world's life forms is restricted to the medium in which it lives, able to see in either air or water but not both. The eyes of terrestrial mammals, for instance – and this includes humans – have curved, lens-like corneas which allow images to be focused on the retina, but which are flattened by the higher underwater pressures.

But the cormorant's cornea is soft, enabling the eye-muscles to adjust the curvature. As a consequence, the bird is able to hunt at, above and well beneath the surface (indeed, cormorants have been observed at a depth of well over 100 metres), so enhancing its feeding opportunities.

Unlike other birds, the cormorant pursues its quarry beneath the water.

Cormorants are excellent swimmers. The Cape species, which is all-black except for a yellow patch of facial skin, is commonly seen in groups skimming low over the inshore waters around the southern African coast. When hunting, it will dive and, unlike most other seabirds (which pounce on their prey) actually pursue and outswim its quarry beneath the surface.

Four other species are found in the region, namely the marginally larger bank cormorant, which is wholly black; the even bigger white-breasted cormorant, an inhabitant of both freshwater and coastal areas, the small and the reed cormorant (freshwater areas only).

C

CROCODILE
Crocodylus niloticus

The Nile crocodile is superbly designed for hunting by ambush. Its eyes, ears and nostrils are so positioned, at the top of its head, that it can lie almost fully submerged in the water for long periods, barely noticeable to the unsuspecting animals, birds – and people – that pass by.

This giant, primeval reptile is active mainly at night, its diet for the most part made up of small and (sometimes) medium-sized mammals that come to the water's edge to drink, and of waterfowl and fish (especially catfish). It catches the larger prey by remaining very still in the water, perhaps floating to resemble a log, and then, with incredible speed, seizing its victim in massive, vice-like jaws and dragging it down to drown in the depths.

For much of the day, though, the croc basks in the sun on the sandbanks in order to gain heat, often in company with others of its kind. For the rest, it lives within its own territory, which it guards, warning others off with short, loud, resonant roars.

Ancient origins

Crocodiles, and their cousins the alligators and the heavily armoured caimans, are the closest living relatives of the long-gone dinosaurs. The Nile species, the only one found in the rivers and wetlands of southern Africa, can grow to a length of six metres and to an age, it is thought, of 100 years and more.

Of all reptilian brains, the crocodile's is the most advanced. The animal can be inquisitive, is able to adapt to different environments and, if caught at a young enough age, will learn to recognize and be comfortable with its keeper.

Mother love

Crocodiles make excellent parents. The female crocodile lays up to 90 hard-shelled eggs in a shallow hole or in the sandy soil of the riverbank, and protects the nest over the three-month incubation period. When she hears her babies begin to hatch, she helps them out and carries them to the water in her mouth. There, the young crocodiles remain in a 'crèche' for several months, defended by the adults as they learn to hunt.

During this time there is close communication between parents and offspring and between the youngsters themselves. The latter begin to squeak even before they hatch, the sounds loud enough to be heard through the shell and covering sand. In the crèche, they call constantly, and as a new batch of hatchlings arrives their elder siblings welcome them with soft greetings. If a predator appears – a large bird of prey, for example – the mother will vibrate her body, creating a tremor which her offspring can feel through the water, at which point the whole brood quickly dives to safety.

CUCKOOS

Family Cuculidae

This bird can perhaps be ranked as nature's most successful con-artist – certainly when it comes to rearing its young. It lays its eggs in the nests of other, entirely different kinds of birds, and the unwitting host is fooled into incubating the egg – and caring for the strange chick.

To do so, the female cuckoo employs remarkable cunning. She chooses a ready-made nest and keeps a watchful eye on it until the selected host birds are about to produce, or have just produced, their clutch. She then waits until they leave on a foraging expedition before darting in to lay her own egg. If the hosts' clutch is already there, she will remove one of the eggs. Timing, of course, is supremely important, but evolution has given the cuckoo a little leeway: she has a built-in mechanism that enables her to keep the replacement egg inside her for about a day – long enough to synchronize the two elements of the exercise to perfection.

And, remarkably, her egg sometimes has colour and markings similar to those of the hosts' clutch, though it is somewhat larger.

> *The cuckoo will fool an unwitting host into incubating its egg – and caring for the cuckoo chick.*

When the cuckoo's chick hatches, it tries hard – and usually with success – to eject the other eggs or, if they have already hatched, the chicks themselves by spreading its wings and pushing them backwards. In fact 'tries' is not the correct word, for the action has a quite different motivation: nature has helped along the ejection process by endowing the baby cuckoo with a small, excruciatingly itchy patch on its back, between its wings. This the youngster tries frantically to 'scratch' by pushing against an object – which, in the nest, is either an egg or another

C

chick. Having thus involuntarily removed the other occupants the cuckoo, as sole tenant, will devour any and all food brought by its hapless foster parents.

Southern Africa is home to 13 species of cuckoo and five species of coucal (which belong to the same family, but are not nest parasites). Among the most attractive is the great spotted cuckoo (*Clamator glandarius*), which is crested. Among the more common is the red-chested cuckoo (*Cuculus solitarius*), better known to locals as the 'piet-my-vrou', a name which echoes its distinctive call. Similarly, the often heard diederik cuckoo (*Chrysococcyx caprius*) is so named for the persistent 'dee-dee-deedereek' sound it makes.

CYCADS

Families Stangeriaceae and Zamiaceae in southern Africa

The often palm-like cycads are the most primitive of all the earth's seed-bearing plants, immensely ancient 'living fossils' that date back to the Carboniferous Period. The group, the first of whose members made their appearance 150 million years ago, reached its ascendancy about 90 million

years later – that is, before the advent of the flowering species – and the plants have scarcely changed in structure or habit since.

Nearly all the great cycad forests of those distant times have long since disappeared, their remains subjected to aeons of heat and pressure to become coal. But a few small patches have survived here and there, most notably (in southern Africa) in the Eastern Cape and near Tzaneen in South Africa's Northern Province, close to the home of Modjadji, renowned Rain Queen of the Lovedu people. The plants have their place in the rain-making rituals. Elsewhere, the starchy pith of the stems is used to make a crude type of bread.

There are about 100 cycad species worldwide. Southern Africa is home to two genera, the larger of which, *Encephalartos*, has 28 species. The Rain Queen's 'Modjadji palms' (*E. transvenosus*) are rather special: they grow to 13 metres in height, and the forest is regarded as one of the subcontinent's botanical wonders.

DAISIES
Family Asteraceae

Perhaps the best known of southern African members of this large flowering plant family is the Namaqualand daisy, which (together with other kinds of daisy) produces wondrous carpets of colour across the western sandveld and neighbouring regions in springtime. Like many of its cousins, the species (*Dimorphotheca sinuata*) is sensitive to light, remains closed at night and when the weather is dull, and turns its face towards the sun on bright days.

All daisies have easily recognizable composite flowers, which are in fact clusters of tiny florets surrounded by often colourful bracts. Among other notable species is the Barberton daisy (*Gerbera jamesonii*), which grows in the north-eastern regions and is a popular garden plant; and the 'bitterkaroo' (*Chrysocoma tenuifolia*), which is found all over the arid interior of South Africa and southern Botswana. Unhappily, it is poisonous to livestock.

Most West Coast daisies are small, low-growing, drought-avoiding plants whose seeds lie dormant during the long dry months and then, after the first rains have fallen and before the onset of the blistering desert breezes, they sense the moistening of the earth and the arrival of the pollinators and burst, briefly, into glorious life.

The Namaqualand daisy is by no means the only flower to decorate the sandveld and other parts of the winter-rainfall succulent Karoo. Indeed the region is home to a breathtaking 4 000 floral species, including mesembryanthemums (fully a third of all the world's known mesembs are found within the Richtersveld, in the far north) and lesser numbers of aloes, perennial herbs, lilies and a host of others.

The daisy remains closed when the weather is overcast, but on bright days opens and turns its face towards the sun.

C

DASSIES
Family Procaviidae

It looks like an oversized guinea-pig, it's easily snapped up by a passing black eagle and, all in all, it has very little going for it – but the humble little dassie can claim a surprisingly noble lineage: despite the absurd difference in size (and shape), its nearest living relative is the mighty elephant!

Of course, the two animals have followed wildly divergent evolutionary routes, but they do have several features in common, including the structure of their feet and teeth (the dassie's are in fact miniature tusks), their blood serology and reproductive cycles.

Most dassies, also known as hyraxes and (some of them) as rock dassies, live among the cliffs and outcrops of southern Africa's rockier areas and are masterly mountaineers: their footpads, moistened by sweat, serve as suction pads, enabling them to scale almost sheer cliff-faces. They are often seen in small groups, in the morning, basking on sunlit koppies (they need to warm up before moving off to feed) throughout the subcontinent. Each group will appoint a 'sentry' who keeps a wary eye open for predatory mammals and, especially, birds of prey. If an eagle or other raptor appears, the whole group will quickly scuttle to the safety of a crevice or, occasionally, simply tumble down the rock face, dropping 15 metres and more without injury.

The southern Africa region is home to two species of rock dassie and one tree dassie, a woollier and more rarely seen animal of the bush and forest. The latter's call, though, is both unmistakable and alarming, a nighttime screech that can chill the blood.

DESERT PLANTS

Life in southern Africa's arid areas — the Great Karoo, the Kalahari, the bone-dry Namib desert — is a constant struggle for survival. The ground holds little or no moisture; the rains are rare and uncertain, and air temperatures veer between boiling hot and icy cold. These conditions have forced the plants and animals to evolve in special and often ingenious ways.

The seeds of the Namaqualand daisy and other desert annuals lie dormant during droughts that can last for years, and then, when the first rains fall, they germinate and burst into glorious flower in a matter of just a few days.

Pollination (the transfer of pollen grains, which contain the male 'gametes', from the anthers of one flower to the stigma of another) and fertilization are essential procedures in the production of seeds, and desert pollinators are kept especially busy.

The pollen of most plants is borne away by the beetles, bees and butterflies, which are a lot more reliable than the wind because they carry it directly from one plant to another, and because the flowering period coincides with the emergence of the insects in numbers. But the plants must compete for the insects' attention, and to do so they have evolved flowers of quite stunning beauty. Among these are the myriad annuals that illuminate the sandy plains of Namaqualand in springtime.

> *Desert plants must compete with each other for the attention of insects, and to do so they have evolved flowers of quite stunning beauty.*

Dispersal of seeds follows shortly after fertilization. For this, some species do indeed rely on the wind, producing lightweight seeds and fruits (usually of the 'parachute' kind) – in vast quantities, because wind-dispersal is very much of a hit-or-miss affair and there is no guarantee that the randomly scattered propagules will carry to suitable habitats in far-off places.

Most ingenious of all are those desert annuals that have developed a delayed-action approach to seed dispersal and germination. For these short-lived plants to depend for species survival on the rare, solitary rain-shower, which could yield only a small amount of precious moisture and may be followed by a drought that persists for several seasons, would be to invite disaster. Wholesale germination would, literally, put all their eggs in one basket.

So they stagger the germination process. They bear different kinds of seeds that, to a greater or lesser degree, will bide their time, some germinating with the first rainfall, others with the next season's rain, still others several seasons down the line.

Their secret: a special substance which occurs in different amounts within the seeds. The substance is designed to stop germination, but is gradually leached out by the rain, so those seeds with smaller amounts of the chemical will germinate at an earlier stage while those with higher concentrations wait for the second, third, fourth or even tenth downpour before releasing their life force. In this way the plants spread their risks, making sure that a high percentage of their progeny will survive the uncertainties of the desert climate.

D

DODO
Raphus cucullatus

'As dead as a dodo' is one of the truer clichés: this large, ground-living bird, once so plentiful on the Indian Ocean island of Mauritius, disappeared into oblivion some four hundred years ago.

The bird, related to the pigeon family, was about the size of a turkey, its plumage dark grey with yellowish-white breast, wings and tufted tail, its beak heavy and hooked, its legs thick and yellow.

A great many dodos inhabited the island when the first European seafarers arrived in 1507, but they were, literally, easy meat: so tame were the birds that they were slaughtered in their thousands by the early settlers, and by the hungry crews of passing ships. The very last of them were seen in the 1680s, though related species survived on other islands of the western Indian Ocean for another century or so.

The only dodo's egg in existence is on display in East London's museum.

DOLPHINS
Family Delphinidae

There are stories aplenty of dolphins going out of their way to rescue humans, of gently but firmly pushing a drowning person to the water's surface. The tales are not so hard to believe (indeed several are well documented), for this is precisely how a mother dolphin helps her newborn baby take its first lungful of air.

Instances of the dolphin's helpfulness to humankind, especially its willingness to co-operate with fishermen – and the rare intelligence with which it does so – have been recorded since the time of the ancient Greeks. Perhaps the most striking modern-day example is the relationship that the fisherfolk of Laguna, a Brazilian coastal town to the south of Rio de Janiero, enjoy with these graceful marine mammals, which regularly and deliberately herd shoals of fish into the nets.

Group living

Not enough is known of the social life of dolphins and their relatives the whales: living as they do in the vastness of the ocean depths, they are hard to study. But it is certain that most species, among them the bottle-nosed dolphin and the orca, or killer whale (largest and swiftest of the Delphinidae family), live in close-knit, socially structured groups or 'schools' that vary in size depending on the availability of food resources, the presence of predators such as sharks and so on.

These and other dolphin species (the southern seas are home to more than a dozen different kinds) also hunt in groups, systematically herding the fish into concentrated shoals, and then nudging them up to the surface before moving in to feed on the squirming mass. According to some sources, studies indicate that such a close understanding between individuals is based on some sort of common 'language' of sounds ranging from low-frequency whistles to high-pitched squeaks, each school 'talking' in its own 'dialect'.

world. If one is to judge by their squeals of delight, the same sense of fun prompts them to surf the bow waves of large ships, a sight familiar to the passengers on many a cruise-liner. The less romantic reality, though, is that in these instances they are simply hitching a free ride (sometimes for distances of 100 kilometres and more) simply to conserve energy.

Broadly speaking, dolphins are noisy for two reasons: to communicate and receive information about the general environment (to locate the fish shoals, for example, and to establish inshore safety zones), and, secondly, to exchange messages with other group members.

A single dolphin can manage about 30 different sounds. Clicks range from rapid, angry sequences conducted between macho males to the cosy affectionate little chuckles of courting couples.

The dolphin's apparent playfulness, and its evident pleasure (and great skill) in performing aquatic acrobatics are legendary – these lovely marine mammals are the star attractions at oceanariums throughout the

DRIVER ANTS
Subfamily Dorylinae

Also known as army or legionary ants, these carnivorous little creatures are notable (as the name suggests) for their military-type discipline: they are a nomadic species, marching across the veld in organized massed columns in their relentless quest for prey.

Driver ants do not operate from a permanent base, though they build temporary nests underground, moving on once they have swept the area clean of the insects and small animals they feed on. The columns are enormous – some colonies are

D

thought to number a staggering 20 million and more individuals – and their passage is terrifyingly purposeful, despite the fact that they appear to have no leader, and even though only a few of the soldier workers are able to see.

These sighted soldiers are bigger than the blind workers (25 to 30 millimetres long, as opposed to the latter's two to eight millimetres), with sausage-shaped bodies, furry heads and big wings. They are among the more common and clumsier of the noisy insects that fly into your house on warm summer nights. The queen is the world's biggest ant, measuring a full 50 millimetres in length, with a hugely distended abdomen that holds her complex battery of reproductive organs. She is able to lay up to four million eggs in a single month.

Similar in some respects, though rather more primitive, is the Matabele ant (subfamily Ponerinae), which also covers the ground in columns, some of them 20 or so metres long. These, though, are specialist feeders, raiding termite mounds and bearing their inhabitants

back to the queen, her retinue of males and the hungry larvae. Each raider will carry up to five termites in its powerful mandibles. When disturbed, the column will break ranks and swarm about in search of the intruder with a menacing, high-pitched squeaking sound.

Southern Africa is home to an enormous number and variety of ant species. Among the most fascinating are members of the subfamily Formicinae, some of which have evolved quite extraordinary methods of gathering and preparing their food. Those whose diet includes honeydew and other substances produced by insects actually 'herd' certain aphids and other small creatures, protecting them from their enemies, even building little shelters for them, in order to ensure a constant supply of their favourite dish.

The workers of other species, known as 'repletes', select some of their fellow ants and feed them vast amounts of honeydew, so that they swell up to gross proportions to serve as 'honeypots' – a reserve larder to be raided in times of food scarcity.

DUNG BEETLES
Subfamily Scarabaeinae

Renowned as the super-efficient vacuum cleaners of the veld, these insects have a quite remarkable ability to locate and remove animal droppings, sometimes converging in numbers (more than 7 000 have been observed at one pile of elephant dung) almost before the animal has completed its motion. Some species then fashion the waste into a ball and roll it away in double-quick time.

In the course of their work the beetles do much for the health of the environment, helping to control the spread of harmful bacteria and other disease vectors. They destroy the eggs of parasites that, left intact, would find their way into the intestines of antelope and other herbivores. And by carrying away the dung they distribute natural fertilizer, returning precious faecal nitrogen to the earth.

Beetle types

The dung beetle belongs to a hugely varied subfamily that embraces some 4 500 different species worldwide, of which about 1 800 are found in Africa and 800 on the southern subcontinent. Some are tiny; others can be as long as six centimetres; all use animal droppings as their main food source – for both themselves and their larvae. Some lay eggs beneath the dung-pat, others inside the pat, and still others – the Scarabaeus species, among them the revered scarab of the ancient Egyptians – dismantle the pat.

The Scarabaeus scoops off a large chunk, up to 40 times its own weight, into a ball and, using its back legs and whirring wings for propulsion, rolls it away to bury it a few centimetres deep in the ground. There, the male and female mate, and feed on the dung cache. They then prepare a 'brood ball', which the female smooths to almost perfect roundness. She makes a hole in the side, deposits a single egg, covers up the hole's entrance and moves off to repeat the process elsewhere. When the egg hatches the grub eats the soft inside of the ball, whose outer surface hardens to form a protective casing.

DWARF MONGOOSE
Helogale parvula

When this endearing little animal, smallest member of the mongoose family and a resident of southern Africa's northern regions, finds a tasty egg that is too big and tough for its jaws, it will hurl it backwards, between its legs, to smash it to pieces against a rock.

On the face of it this is only modestly remarkable, but it does beg far-reaching questions about instinct and the ability to learn – about animal intelligence.

Smashing an egg is not an instinctive act: it is a demonstration of complex behaviour which the mongoose has *learned* from watching the adults.

Ingenious aids to survival

Instances of 'cleverness' abound throughout the natural world.

D

Certain cormorant species, when diving deep for fish, will overcome the body's buoyancy by swallowing pebbles to create ballast. Sea otters, which feed largely on spiny sea-urchins, will neutralize the poisonous spikes by wrapping seaweed around their tips and breaking off the bases. The spectacled bears of South America have been known to use sticks to knock fruit down from the trees. The Egyptian vulture, now rare in the region but occasionally seen from the Eastern Cape province north and northwestwards, is renowned for the way it eats the eggs of ground-living birds (including those of ostriches): it selects a suitable stone and hurls it repeatedly at the egg until the shell breaks. Just as ingenious is the bearded vulture or lammergeier (see page 63), which drops the larger bones from a prodigious height onto the rocks far below, shattering them into swallowable pieces.

Rats (and squirrels) are famous for the way they can negotiate a lengthy series of obstacles, each one calling for a 'reasoned' decision, in order to get to the prize at the end.

And so on: there are countless examples of quite extraordinary improvisation to be found in the wild kingdom.

The thinking primate

These feats of ingenuity are not of course the product of rational thought, but nevertheless it seems we gravely underestimate the brain-power of many of our fellow animals, especially the primates.

> Monkeys have been trained to look after their wheelchair-bound owners in various ways around the house.

A mother monkey (in this case, a South American capuchin) was observed tending her injured baby in uncannily human fashion, pressing a compact of mud and leaves onto the open wound. An octopus has been taught to open a corked bottle to get at the shrimp inside. An elephant will pick up a stick in order to scratch itself – a clear instance of tool-use.

Indeed, some primates show an astonishing capacity to learn, and to act on their new knowledge. A chacma baboon was taught by his crippled master, a South African railway employee, to work the track signals (see page 12); monkeys have been trained to look after their wheelchair-bound owners in many and various ways around the house; in the wild, young baboons, intent on secret mischief, will sometimes give a false alarm to distract the attention of the troop – a ploy which calls for deliberate calculation.

Apes in their natural environment often use tools. A chimp will sometimes choose and prepare a stick (it peels off the bark and frays one end of its 'fishing rod') to probe termite mounds for food; mother chimps teach their young to crack nuts with the aid of a rock (only certain rocks are selected); if the bank of a stream or waterhole is too high for a chimp to bend down to drink, it will sometimes manufacture a 'sponge' by chewing a wad of leaves, dipping it into the water and carrying the moisture to the mouth, and so on.

A mother monkey tended her injured baby, in uncannily human fashion, by pressing a compact onto the wound.

Chimpanzees, closest of humankind's relatives, will also use sticks and stones as weapons – as does the humbler baboon, though usually to defend itself rather than to attack. Most amazing of all are the apes who in various, well publicised experiments conducted over the years, have mastered the rudiments of human language, making themselves clearly understood with sounds, signs, symbols and on the computer keyboard.

ELAND
Tragelaphus oryx

This handsome animal is the largest of Africa's antelopes: a male bull will tip the scales at around 700 kilograms (more than ten times heavier than the average man) and reach 1,7 metres in height at the shoulder.

Eland are a social species, often forming large herds in habitats that range from the open savanna country north of South Africa's Orange River to the light woodlands of KwaZulu-Natal and neighbouring Mozambique. They also occur widely in Central and East Africa.

Although most are rufous-brown, old males sometimes take on a greyish-blue colour. Both sexes have heavy, slightly spiralled horns (the male's are much larger than the female's), and develop a dewlap and a slight hump behind the head.

D

ELEPHANT
Loxodonta africana

Legend has it that elephants go to special places – graveyards – when they sense the coming of death. There is no substance to this tale, but these giants of the African savannas do show an unusual sensitivity towards, or curiosity about, the bones of their own kind.

An elephant group will often appear to be fascinated by the bleached carcass of a long-dead animal, shuffling the bones about with their trunks and even moving them away into denser bush. They pay special attention to the jawbone.

Elephants appear to be even more conscious of and moved by the actual process of death within their own group. Family members of a dying animal will trumpet their distress, and have been known to support the weakening creature, keeping it on its feet, even to fill its mouth with grass. And, when it finally succumbs and falls to the ground, they are loth to abandon the corpse, gently touching it with their trunks, sometimes for hours.

When a calf sickens or is hurt, the adults will gather around in a protective circle. If it dies, the mother will, again, stay with the body, guarding it against predatory intruders and even, it has been reported, carry the dead infant around on her tusks.

Facts and figures

The African elephant is the largest of all land mammals, weighing up to six tonnes and reaching an average shoulder height of 3,3 metres (a record 4,42 in the case of one Namibian specimen). Tusk size varies according to age, environment and heredity: those of the famous bull named Mufanyane, who died in South Africa's Kruger National Park in 1983, were a perfectly matched 55,1 kilograms each; the largest tusks on record, of an animal shot in Kenya in 1897, have a combined weight of 199,8 kilograms (they are kept in the British Museum in London). Elephants are voracious and destructive feeders: a single adult will eat anything up to 300 kilograms of grass, shoots and bark each day, and will even push over a whole tree to get to the tender leaves at the top. They are also fond of water, drinking as much as 200 litres of it in a day, wading and luxuriating in it, and squirting it over their bodies and, especially, over their ears to keep themselves cool. The ears are then flapped to enhance the cooling effect. In dry areas they appear to be able to detect the presence of underground water and will methodically dig for it.

Sociable by nature, elephants form groups of females and their offspring – usually of between 10 and 20 animals – that are led by a mature cow, or matriarch. Mature bulls, which only associate with the females for mating purposes, either get together in bachelor groups or, less often, become solitary. Several of these family herds will inhabit a kind of clan territory, sometimes coming together in aggregations of several hundred individuals.

FIREFLIES
Family Lampyridae

These little creatures, and their relatives the glow-worms, are remarkable for their ability to create light – and to use it to recognize one another.

The firefly's flashing light enables males and females to find each other.

Despite their common names, fireflies and glow-worms are types of beetle. Their luminosity is 'cold' (practically no heat is generated), a 'pure' light produced by a reaction between a chemical substance called luciferin, contained in the tip of the abdomen, and luciferase, an enzyme in the blood.

The mechanism is vital in the mating process, enabling male and female fireflies of the same species – of which there are about 30 in the southern African region – to find each other. The male's glow is intermittent, flashing as he moves around in the dark; the female's glow is weaker and she remains immobile, patiently waiting for her prospective partner's arrival.

According to researchers, each firefly species' flash frequency is different, and seen to be so by the insects, so there is very little chance of mistaken identity.

Glow-worms are rather different: only the female produces light, a strong, steady glow that serves as a beacon to the lightless male. These species get their common name from the worm-like shape of the wingless female. The male rather resembles the firefly in appearance.

E

FISH EAGLE

Haliaeetus vocifer

This raptor is among the best known – and certainly the most photographed – of southern Africa's birds, and generally regarded as the supreme aerial predator. Its routine is certainly dramatic enough. Yet, in truth, most of the birds spend very little of their time actually hunting.

This large species (it has a wingspan of around 2,4 metres), which can be seen in wetlands and near rivers, dams and lagoons throughout the subcontinent, is immediately recognizable by its black, white and chestnut plumage and its stubby tail. For the most part it preys on live fish, swooping down at a narrow angle to within a few centimetres of the water's surface and, without a check in its flight, grasping the victim in powerful talons to carry it up to the perch. It is this spectacular sequence, together with the eagle's scream, that accounts for its celebrity status and the wide coverage it gets in the press and on screen. Its keening call, the quintessential sound of the raw African continent, is heard most often at dawn and in flight.

Image and reality

Contrary to the image, however, the fish eagle does not always behave as a predator. When its favoured food is in short supply it will happily rob other birds, notably herons and cormorants, of their catches, steal their eggs, kill and eat their nestlings, hunt other waterbirds and, occasionally, take frogs, insects and a variety of land creatures ranging from monkeys to large monitor lizards (leguaans) and dassies (hyraxes). Nor is it averse to scavenging.

In normal times, though, fish eagles – those living in the permanent wetlands – devote only a small fraction of their time to the search for food (one Kenyan study came up with an average of just eight minutes a day!). They are highly sedentary birds, rarely moving away from the narrow limits of their clearly defined territories. Indeed, a pair may well stay in the same small patch of watery terrain for its entire lifespan.

In southern Africa, fish eagles lay their clutch of between one and three (but usually two) plain white eggs in winter and, as with other African accipiters, though perhaps rather less so, sibling aggression often leads to the death of the weakest (last-born) chick. The nest, a large affair of sticks, is built high up in one of the taller trees, sometimes on a cliff-ledge, and is occupied by the same pair for years on end.

Unhappily, as with so many birds of prey, the species is threatened by human interference. Pesticides and other pollutants find their way into the waterways, contaminate the fish and are eventually absorbed by the eagles. The result: thinner shells and more easily damaged eggs.

FROGS

Most of us associate frogs with a watery environment, but in fact many of these hardy amphibians are perfectly able to survive in the most arid of conditions.

Dryland frogs live through the long southern African droughts by burrowing into the ground and, when the soil dries up, entering a state of dormancy or 'suspended animation' (the technical term is 'aestivation') in which their vital organs, such as heart, lungs and kidneys, stop functioning. And in order to keep the moisture held by their bodies, they wrap themselves in a waterproof sheath, which they fashion from the outer layers of their skin.

Thus cocooned, and without the need to make any energy-sapping movements, they happily sleep away the long waterless spells – which, in the arid north-western regions, can last for months and even years. With the coming of the first rains they emerge from their undeground hideaways none the worse for wear.

In the desert, the first downpour may be the only one for a long time to come, and the frogs must make the most of the brief bonanza, eating as much and as quickly as they can. The bullfrog, a giant member of the Ranidae group, is the most voracious of all during the breeding season, snapping up anything that moves – insects, mice, lizards, birds, other bullfrogs and even, if you approach too closely, the ends of your fingers. The actual breeding process is also a frenetic affair: eggs hatch within two days of mating, and the tadpoles take less than 18 days to turn into fully-fledged adults.

Select species

The bullfrog (*Pyxicephalus adspersus*) differs from other southern African species in that the male is bigger than the female and, unusually, is known to protect the eggs and tadpoles from potential predators. Its loud call, similar to the bellow of a calf, gives it its common name. The largest recorded southern African specimen measured nearly 20 centimetres – impressive enough, but hardly a match for West Africa's huge 25,4-cm Conrava goliath monster, largest of the world's frogs.

Among the most fascinating of southern species is the large grey tree frog (*Chiromantis xerampelina*), which

F

has fingers well adapted for climbing, can actually grasp twigs, and spends most of its life in trees. During the mating process, the female chooses a branch overhanging water, and there she produces a sticky fluid which the male and several of his friends, in a remarkable co-operative effort, churn into a foam with their hindlegs. She then lays her eggs in the foam-nest, which bakes to a hardness in the morning sun, thus providing her hatching offspring with protection as well as moisture. About two days later the tadpoles emerge and drop down into the water.

Perhaps the most attractive of southern African species are the often brilliantly hued reed frogs of the genus *Hyperolius* whose common names – waterlily frog, arum frog, reed frog and so on – indicate their natural habitats.

Many types of frog have the ability to manufacture poisons from glands in the skin; perhaps the most toxic southern African species is the brightly coloured red-and-black banded rubber frog (*Phrynomantis bifasciatus*). The rain frogs (*Breviceps* spp.) also produce substances poisonous enough to deter predators.

Notable for its contribution to science is South Africa's common platanna (*Xenopus laevis*), a primitive frog which hopped into the limelight when it was first used in human pregnancy tests. In these, the female platanna is injected with a sample of the woman's urine and, if she is indeed pregnant, the frog begins laying eggs within six to 12 hours. If not, no eggs are produced.

GEMSBOK
Oryx gazella

It is said that the myth of the unicorn – the splendid horse with a solitary horn held proudly aloft – derived from the Arabian oryx, relative of southern Africa's gemsbok. And indeed, when you view this antelope in profile, with its scimitar-like horns positioned in line, it does recall the fabled beast. Like the unicorn, too, it is a fine-looking animal, stately in its bearing, striking in its black, grey and white markings, dangerous in its needle-sharp armoury.

Some gemsbok have horns fully 100 centimetres long, and they have been known to impale an attacking lion. This antelope's principal enemy, though, is the spotted hyaena, which it confronts by facing head-on to the pack, sometimes with its back against a tree or shrub. It lowers its head so that the needle-sharp horns are level with the ground and chest-high to the predators, and then swings its head from side to side in a dangerous scything motion. It will also, sometimes, launch itself forward in a brief, ferocious charge.

The gemsbok is a creature of the arid regions – of the Northern Cape, the Kalahari and Namibia – and it is quite superbly adapted to the harshness of the desert. It is able to survive quite happily for months on end without drinking water, obtaining the moisture it needs from the plants that, somehow, manage to survive and grow and even to thrive in these desolate places.

Keeping cool

And it has adapted to the sandy wastelands in other ways. Its low metabolic rate – unusually low for an animal of its bulk (adult bulls weigh in at around 240 kilograms) – lessens its need for food and water. The workings of its body (physiology) and its behaviour patterns are geared to conserving fluids and energy. The animal avoids the heat of the day, lying up in shade or, where there are no trees, so positioning itself that the smallest possible area of its body is presented to the sun. On especially hot days the gemsbok's body temperature rises above normal – to a remarkable 45° Centigrade – so that it does

not waste precious water by panting. It can do this without ill effect because a vulnerable part of its brain, the hypothalamus, is protected by a feature known as the 'carotid rete'. This curious mechanism, present in a number of other animals (including sheep, a variety of ungulates and even some cats), consists of a maze of fine blood vessels that, together, act as an efficient heat-exchange unit, cooling the blood with moisture from the nasal passages.

GIRAFFE

Giraffa camelopardalis

Although it is the tallest of all the earth's creatures, the giraffe can nevertheless make itself surprisingly inconspicuous in its natural habitat. It is a master of camouflage: the way it is able to stand perfectly still, together with its dappled coat – a beautiful lattice-work of irregular patches – enable it to blend into and become an almost indistinguishable part of its savanna woodland surrounds.

The giraffe lives in groups of varying sizes (usually six to ten animals, but sometimes much larger), its favoured food the tender leaves, shoots and flowers of the tree's upper parts – a diet that has led to the

49

F

evolution of its freakishly long neck. This feature is among the clearest examples of what is known as natural selection: over countless generations the taller animals could take in more nourishment, were better able to survive droughts, better able to breed, and so those genes that produced the longer neck became increasingly prominent within the species' gene well.

Nature's ingenuity

This in turn triggered other, not so obvious but equally remarkable physical changes. For example, in order to compensate for the huge distance between heart and head, nature has devised a rather special adaptation of the arteries to pump blood up to the brain, plus a unique arrangement of valves in the larger veins to prevent the blood from running back. Without this mechanism, the giraffe's brain would be either starved of blood when the animal stands erect, or flooded, lethally so, when it bends down to drink.

To pump the blood so far uphill to the brain also calls for some ingenious biological engineering. Thus its heart is unusually large (about two to three per cent of body mass) and tough (its walls are a good seven centimetres thick).

The giraffe's main enemy is the lion, to which it is especially vulnerable when it is slaking its thirst at river-bank or waterhole. In order to get down far enough to drink it has to splay its legs out, a position which renders it virtually helpless. Away from water, though, it is more than able to hold its own: it is fleet of foot (its name is derived from the Arabic word 'xirapha', which means 'one who moves swiftly'), it has a great deal of stamina, and it can deliver a deadly kick with both its fore- and hindlimbs.

Social life

Although giraffes are found in groups (of anything between four and 50), the composition of the herds is flexible, with much movement between them. Adult bulls, which spend a lot of their time alone, are not territorial: instead, there is a complicated ranking system that governs access to the females. Bulls indulge in 'necking', a ritualistic fight that establishes dominance within the group.

There are eight (some authorities say nine) fairly distinct subspecies, or races, of giraffe in Africa, distinguished most obviously by the colour and structure of their markings (Kenya's reticulated giraffe is among the more striking). Most of the populations are confined to parks and other protected areas; elsewhere they are on the decline as the trees of the savanna regions are cut down for firewood, for building material, and to clear the ground for planting. In parts of Africa they are also hunted for their meat, for their tough hides – and, sad to say, for the tails, which make fine fly-whisks.

GRAPPLE-THORN

Harpagophytum procumbens

In an extraordinary example of how even plants can find ingenious solutions to the harshness of their environment, the grapple-thorn, commonly known as devil's claw, has evolved a stunningly original way of spreading its seeds.

The grapple-thorn, a resident of the Kalahari region's arid dunelands, belongs to the sesame family (though you wouldn't think so to look at it), and its underground tuber sends out long, creeping stems.

To these are attached the seed-pods, each armed with wicked little grapple hooks that fasten firmly onto the hoofs of a passing antelope. Eventually the pods will be trampled underfoot, their seeds scattered across the dry, sandy earth, and in due course they germinate.

In such a manner does this plant reproduce itself over a wide area. Often, though, the hooks remain embedded and can set up a fatal infection in the antelope. And occasionally they will grip and infect a grazing animal's mouth, killing it by slow starvation.

The fleshy tubers of the devil's claw are in demand as a herbal reme-dy – an infusion of the dried material is used to treat rheumatic ailments, and as a general health tonic – and human harvesters have pretty well eradicated the plant in much of its range.

GROUND SQUIRREL

Xerus inauris

Most animals in the hotter, drier parts of southern Africa move in and out of shade in order to lose excess heat and maintain a constant body temperature (which is essential to their wellbeing). Some also take sand-baths, lying belly-down and splay-legged on the cooler ground. The Cape ground squirrel, however, has a unique answer to the fierceness of the sun: it carries its own shade around – its large, bushy tail serves as a kind of parasol, which it waves in gentle arcs above its back and head while out feeding.

The shade so provided lowers this attractive, alert little animal's temperature by a couple of degrees, so allowing it to forage for longer periods – a distinct advantage over other creatures competing for the same food supplies. The parasol may also allow it to stay out during those hours when the large birds of

G

prey, its chief enemies, have retired into the cool canopies of the trees.

When the open ground becomes just too hot for the squirrel – in some areas temperatures at the surface can reach a blistering 70° Centigrade – it will retire into the nearest patch of deep shade, lie on its belly with its legs stretched out and throw cool sand over itself. For the rest, it lives in a labyrinthine burrow in the company of up to 30 other squirrels under the rule of a dominant (known as the alpha) female.

The burrow functions as a refuge against marauding birds as well as a nighttime shelter, though it provides scant protection against the squirrels' other deadly enemy, the snake. But the animals have an effective, if rather curious, way of dealing with an attack from this quarter: the one nearest to the reptile will imitate the snake's crawling movement by sweeping its tail back and forth. For some reason this unnerves the snake, which usually retires in confusion.

HAMERKOP
Scopus umbretta

The hamerkop, one of the oddest-looking of Africa's species, is a fairly large, brown-coloured, solitary bird with a crest on its head which, with its short neck and long, flattened beak, gives it the profile of a hammer (hence its Afrikaans common name).

You will often see the bird standing motionless in the shallow parts of inland lakes and waterways, apparently lost in thought but now and again stirring up the mud to disturb its prey – small creatures such as frogs and aquatic insects.

The hamerkop is known as 'the bird of doom' to some rural folk, though just why it has earned this grim epithet remains unexplained. It may have something to do with its strange appearance, or with its call, an eerie jumble of hisses, squeaks and frog-like croaks that speak of spirits in torment. Or perhaps it is because the bird collects bones (among much else: see further on) to build its nest, a habit associated in some parts of Africa with witchcraft. However that may be, to disturb it is apparently an invitation to disaster.

The hamerkop is unique: it is confined to Africa and Madagascar, and it is the only member of its family (Scopidae). It is also one of the more accomplished architects of the natural world. It builds its nest slowly and carefully, taking anything between four and six weeks to complete an enormous, domed home of grass, reeds, mud and bits of rubbish such as old bones, rags, pieces of plastic and other throw-outs from human society. The ingredients of one hamerkop's nest, found in Bulawayo, Zimbabwe, was described by the author Warwick Tarboton in his book *Waterbirds*; it contained, apart from the conventional material used, the grass and twigs and so on, 'one pan brush, one broken cassette tape, one glove, one plastic dish, one plastic cup, two peacock feathers, chicken feathers, two socks, rabbit fur, 45 rags, four mealie cobs, one piece of glass, four bits of wire, one plastic comb, one pair of male underpants, one typewriter ribbon, one piece of leather belt, four stockings, two pieces of tin, two pieces of foam rubber, seven pieces of hosepipe, nine pieces of electrical pipe, six pieces of asbestos roofing, 11 bones, 12 pieces of sandpaper, four pieces of insulation tape, 10 plastic bags, nine pieces of paper, 56 scraps of tinfoil, six bicycle tyres and six lengths of insulating wire'. Quite a collection.

The nest, sited in a tree or on a ledge, weighs around 50 kilograms, can be two metres in diameter, has massively thick, virtually impregnable walls and can bear the weight of a full-grown man. Construction work is often a co-operative effort by four or more of the birds. Contrary to popular belief the structure does not have three chambers but only one, which is mud-plastered with a 50-centimetre long entrance tunnel facing outwards and downwards – in other words, so positioned as to make access by unwelcome intruders as difficult as possible.

HIPPOPOTAMUS

Hippopotamus amphibius

The yawn of a hippo is an awesome sight: this semi-aquatic mammal will suddenly rear out of the water and open its cavernous mouth to reveal a collection of tusk-like teeth that can (and occasionally do) chew a small river-craft to pieces.

Humans yawn because their bodies demand more oxygen, but among many animals the gesture is also a means of communication. In the male hippo's case the message depends on the company it's keeping. If this is a female, the yawn is part of the courtship ritual, conveying something of what we would call 'affection'. If on the other hand there are other bulls on the scene the gaping mouth is a 'back off' signal. Fights between adult males,

G

for dominance of a territory, are rare but when they do happen they are spectacularly ferocious affairs, full of sound and fury, and terrible injuries can be inflicted.

Shrinking habitats

The hippopotamus was once common throughout the wetter parts of the continent, a familiar feature of the African scene from the mouth of the Nile down to the Cape Peninsula (the first Dutch settlers complained nervously of the 'roaring of sea-cows'). But over the decades it disappeared from much of the continent, pushed out by hunters and human settlement. In southern Africa it is now found only in the northern parts of KwaZulu-Natal, the Kruger National Park, southern Mozambique, the riverine and wetland areas of Botswana (notably the Okavango Delta), the Caprivi and Zambesi regions, and in a select number of sanctuaries.

The species is usually seen in schools of between two and five, but sometimes more than 20, basking in or alongside water during the day. At night the animals forage near a river or pan, although when grazing is scarce – and it has a healthy appetite: a full feed for one adult is around 140 kilograms – it will travel up to 40 kilometres in search of good grass.

Oddly enough, the animal may not restrict its diet entirely to vegetation: there have been recent and reliable reports of hippos feeding on impala antelope - and even, very occasionally, on other hippos!

The wanderer

Some individuals, indeed, can wander even farther afield. Especially enterprising was Hubert, who captured world headlines between 1928 and 1931 when 'he' embarked on a 2 000-kilometre odyssey through Zululand, Natal and the eastern Cape. His confident and gentle meanderings, which included digressions along byways and through many adventures (at one point he turned up in the streets of Durban!) eventually and sadly ended when he was shot by hunters near King William's Town, at which point it was discovered that 'he' was a female and her name was changed to Huberta.

But water is the hippo's milieu. Indeed, these animals cannot remain on dry land for very long during the daytime as their thick skin is highly sensitive to the hot sun. They are of course excellent swimmers, though they invariably breathe out when diving to allow them to walk along the river-bed, which they do at a fair pace. They can remain beneath the surface for five minutes and more.

Mother and child

The female gives birth to a single calf in the shallows or in a secluded, trampled clearing in the reed beds (where the mother may hide it for a few days), and it is able to swim within a few minutes. For a time she will suckle her offspring while lying on the bottom, the calf coming to the surface for air every half-minute or so.

It is popularly believed that a hippo will carry the infant on her back, but this is something of a myth. What happens is that, in cold weather, the baby will often expose the front part of its body to the warm sunshine by clambering halfway up its mother's body.

Hippo hazards

Hippos are generally placid enough, posing little threat to humans. They can be very dangerous, though, if their path back to water is blocked, or while grazing at night – a time when they are not at their most alert. Their first reaction to a sudden confrontation is to bite (a horrific prospect). In some regions, especially those where they have suffered harassment, they may attack boats.

Elsewhere in Africa (notably in Tanzania) there are tentative schemes to 'farm' hippos – for their meat, hides, the ivory of their teeth, and for bone-meal and curios. The ivory is apparently of a better quality than the elephant's (as is that of the

> *Hippos can be very dangerous, especially if their path back to water is blocked.*

warthog). The experiments seem to make considerable economic sense as these animals have plenty of bulk, breed fairly frequently, have a relatively brief gestation period and grow quickly to maturity.

HONEY BADGER
Mellivora capensis

Pound for pound the honey badger must rank among the two or three toughest of African mammals. It is a small (12-kilogram), compact bundle of energy, muscle and courage which, when cornered, will confront any threat with teeth bared, snarling defiance and sometimes charging – quite regardless of the size and strength of its persecutor.

However, despite its reputation for aggressiveness, the badger is generally shy, preferring to retire into a hole when disturbed – or to use its second line of defence: apart from its razor-sharp teeth and lethal claws, its anal glands, like those of the polecat and skunk, produce smells noxious enough to intimidate large predators.

As the name suggests, the animal has a fondness for honey, seeking out beehives and ripping them apart to gorge itself on their contents. The bees will attack, of course, but the badger's thick hide is more or less impervious to their stings. Its sweet tooth has encouraged an intriguing relationship with the greater honeyguide, a little bird that shows the way to the hives with excited displays, watches while the animal destroys the nest, and then joins in the feast.

For all that, though, the honey badger is primarily a meat-eater. It is strong enough to bring down a small buck, but its usual diet is made up of a range of small animals and invertebrates – rodents, lizards, snakes (it is capable of dispatching a three-metre long python), spiders, grubs and bee larvae. It will also eat fruits, bulbs and roots. Much of this food has to be dug out of the ground with its powerful front claws – and other creatures besides the honeyguide, among them chanting goshawks and the occasional jackal, follow the digging expeditions, gobbling up escapees from the excavations.

HONEY BEES
Apis mellifera

So structured, so rigidly regimented and collectively purposeful is a hive of honey bees that the whole colony, which numbers tens of thousands of individuals, can in some ways be regarded as a single organism.

Honey bee society is divided into three castes – the queen, the drones (males) and workers (sterile females), each of which has a preordained and strictly regulated function.

The hive is ruled by a solitary queen, who is much larger than her fellow bees. The drones' only purpose in life is to fertilize the queen, enabling her to lay the eggs (up to 2 000 a day) that will produce the next generation. Drones are also large, and relatively few in number.

Female home-makers
Much smaller and more numerous are the sterile female workers, whose role it is to build the multi-celled honeycombs (from wax produced in their bodies), and find and collect nectar from flowers and convert it into honey, which they store away in the comb's hexagonal cells. These also serve as compartments for the newly laid eggs, and nurseries for the growing larvae, which the workers' continue to feed with honey, pollen and a protein-rich substance called 'royal jelly' (which they themselves produce, in their mouth-glands). The cells built for future queens are larger, and their inmates are fed only with royal jelly. Those destined to become drones also get more living space.

The stages in a female worker's life are also strictly regulated. After hatching, the larva will do nothing but solicit food from the older workers but soon enough, within two or three days, she will begin to prepare empty brood cells in readiness for new eggs. Shortly thereafter her glands begin to develop, and she's able to feed royal jelly to the queen and the larvae (a diet that continues to be enjoyed by the young queens-to-be; drone and worker larvae quickly progress to a more humble regimen of pollen). When she is 12 days old, the young worker is able to produce wax, and she begins constructing and capping new comb-cells. She can also process nectar to produce honey. A week later she will take on guard duty, and at three weeks of age will venture out into the field to forage for nectar.

Changing the guard

The hive never contains more than one queen, but her subjects don't wait for her to die before appointing her successor. She may die from accident or old age, of course, but usually one of the queens-in-waiting either destroys her during her normal life-span or, more often, forces her to leave the nest. In the latter event, she departs with an escort of workers (who have prepared well for their journey, filling their honey sacs from the storage cells).

The old queen and her faithful followers are the nucleus of a new colony. Soon the escorting workers will have located a suitable nest site, and the cycle of life will begin again, in a new hive some distance away.

Meanwhile, the virgin queen will wait a while before leaving the original colony to mate with one of the drones. She stores his sperm in her body and returns to the old hive, at which point the other potential queens, no longer needed (they were only reared in case of an accident on the mating flight) are killed off.

HONEYGUIDE
Family Indicatoridae

The common name for these rather drab-looking little birds is derived from the remarkable ability of two species, the greater honey-guide (*Indicator indicator*) and the scaly throated honeyguide (*I. variegatus*), to bring man and animal, notably the honey-badger, to bees' nests. When it locates such a nest, the bird will search for a human or a badger and, having found one, perform a fluttering display as it flies from tree to tree, keeping up a ceaseless

H

chattering as it leads the way to the nest. If its prospective helper declines to follow, the honeyguide becomes visibly upset.

Once the helper has broken open the nest and taken the honey, the bird moves in to feast on the beeswax and grubs left behind.

Honeyguides have short bills and unusually tough skins, an adaptive feature that probably developed to protect them from bee-stings. Like cuckoos, they lay their eggs in other birds' nests, and some species (the larger ones) have hooks at the tips of both the upper and lower beaks, apparently designed to kill off the host's chicks.

Six species of honey-guide occur in southern Africa, the four most common being the two men-tioned, the sharp-billed honeyguide (*Prodotiscus regulus*) and the lesser honey-guide (*I. minor*).

more unusual hunters, snaring (or 'corralling') rather than out-swimming its fish prey.

To do so, it gets together with a few others of its kind to create a 'bubble net', the group releasing a great cloud of bubbles from their blowholes as they swim around a shoal of fish. The rising bubbles 'herd' the shoal into a concentrated mass, which makes the fish much easier to catch. The whales can

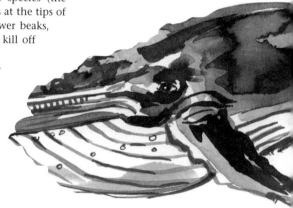

HUMPBACK WHALE

Megaptera novaeangliae

This great marine mammal, which can reach 18 metres in length (though the average for an adult male in the southern seas is around 13 metres), is one of the ocean's

also vary the size of the bubbles to suit the size of their prey – very much like a fisherman will choose a net of just the right mesh for his intended catch.

Humpback whales are renowned for the sounds, or 'songs', they produce beneath the water. These are moans and melodious wails, of varying pitch, that can sometimes last for a full half-hour. Such 'music' is highly distinctive, differing from group

to group and locality to locality, and indeed the patterns change over a period of time. Scientists reckon that because these songs appear to progress, or evolve, they represent a form of communication, perhaps even 'conversation', between whales of the same stock. Whale songs travel hundreds of kilometres beneath the ocean and, it has been suggested, may be the cetacean equivalent of our long-distance telephone calls.

IMPALA

Aepyceros melampus

Few visitors to the savanna woodlands spare a second glance for the herds of these medium-sized antelope. In many places they are such a familiar sight that they become part of the landscape. But they are worth a much closer look, for they are beautiful, bright-eyed and alert, delicate of form and feature and, in movement, among the most graceful of all Africa's animals.

Startle a herd of these antelope in a bush-covered area and they will bound away across the veld in a series of prodigious leaps, often rising effortlessly three metres into the air – a quite extraordinary height for so large a species. And to add to the spectacle they move in perfect unison, covering the ground in an almost ballet-like, choreographed sequence of sweeping ascents, descents and fluid changes in direction to create sheer poetry in motion.

For the most part impala are gentle creatures, living peacefully with each other, the rams in bachelor herds, the ewes and their lambs in breeding herds. But the tranquillity is deceptive: come the autumn rutting (mating) season and the males undergo a dramatic Jekyll-and-Hyde

H

kind of personality change, each competing noisily and aggressively for a prime piece of turf, and for his own 'harem' of 15 to 20 ewes, with a cacophony of loud snorts, growls, barks and roars. The sounds can be quite disconcerting: more than one tourist has mistaken them for the roars of an unseen lion.

Only male impala have horns, which are elegantly lyre-shaped and deeply ringed. Those of the East African race are especially long. The far western race, many protected within Namibia's Etosha National Park, has a distinctively black face.

JACANAS
Family Jacanidae

These unusual birds, inhabitants of southern Africa's wetlands, have freakishly long toes that enable them to walk, and run, on floating plants without sinking. They are popularly known as lily-trotters. Of the two resident species, the African jacana (*Actophilornis africanus*) is by far the

more common and conspicuous, occurring in, among other places, Botswana's Okavango swamps, northern Namibia, Mozambique, and in eastern Mpumalanga, KwaZulu-Natal and the Transkei region of South Africa's Eastern Cape.

The brown-and-white, long-necked bird is also a good swimmer – and a good flyer, easily (and noisily) taking to the air – with its legs and toes trailing while emitting a sharp, ringing flight-call. It is an unusual bird, too, in its breeding habits. The female, which is the larger and more aggressive of the sexes, will lay up to ten clutches in a single season, taking on a succession of different partners. And on each occasion the roles are reversed: it is the male jacana that looks after the eggs. The female's huge workload sometimes proves too much for her, so that by the end of the season she is weak, and vulnerable to predators.

Smaller, rarer and more elusive is the lesser jacana (*Microparra capensis*), which has a distinctive white belly, breast and throat but is secretive in habit and often goes unnoticed. It is found in lagoons and marshlands in the northern and eastern parts of the subcontinent.

JELLYFISH
Coelenterates of the class Scyphozoa

These marine creatures, which do not look like and are not in any way related to true fish, are among the most primitive of the larger life forms. They are capable of delivering a poisonous sting, though most are harmless to humans. A few, however, can prove deadly. They range in size from the microscopic organisms to saucer-shaped monsters measuring three metres across.

Adult jellyfish are also known as medusae, after one of the mythological Gorgons who had snakes for hair. Technically, they belong to the coelenterates, a lowly group that has many forms, including the corals, and whose name means 'hollow animal', a reference to its large central body cavity or stomach.

Jellyfish can swim – by contracting and expanding their bodies – but only weakly, and for the most part they depend for movement on tide and current. They capture their food, which comprises any small marine creature with which they come into contact, by injecting and stunning it with their venom

The really dangerous jellyfish are members of the Cubomedusae group, which have cube-shaped bodies and long tentacles full of powerful venom. The 'sea wasp', found in Australian waters, can quickly kill a full-grown man. The most that southern African bathers have to fear, though, is the sting of a blue-bottle, or Portuguese man o' war, a relative of the jellyfish (see page 84).

JUMPING SPIDERS
Family Salticidae

These acrobatic, bungee-jumping hunting spiders do not spin webs or build traps but rely, instead, on their agility and remarkable eyesight to catch their food.

Their bodies are compact and hairy, and they have a huge pair of stereoscopic eyes (plus three much smaller ones) set in their flat faces. Get close enough to one and, because of the way light reflects from the back of the movable retina, the creature appears to be following your movements with intelligent intensity, producing an unnervingly human-like impression.

Jumping spiders, most of which are tiny, stalk and then leap upon their prey with electrifying speed and often over long distances. Before doing so, they fix a disc-like 'anchor' to the ground and spin a silk anchor-line. In this way they can always bring themselves back to their place of safety, whether they have missed their target or not.

Some species of jumping spider are excellent mimics. Those which prey on ants imitate their victims by changing colour and taking on a typically ant-like posture, holding up their front legs to represent 'feelers'. They even adopt the ants' scurrying, searching movement patterns.

KILLER WHALE

Orcinus orca

Despite its common name, this fierce predator of the ocean depths is not a whale but a dolphin (it's the largest member of the Dolphinidae family). It can weigh up to 10 tonnes, reach 10 metres in length, is armed with large, conical teeth – and is the terror of the seas. Its most striking physical feature is the black and white markings of its body – patterns that represent a 'fingerprint' unique to a particular animal (they are used by researchers throughout the world to identify individuals).

The more amiable side of the killer whale, or orca, was movingly portrayed in the film *Free Willy*, and in captivity the species appears docile, lovable, and easily trainable – and, to patrons of oceanariums, it is a hugely entertaining animal. Once or twice, though, a captive orca has 'played' with its trainer, keeping him beneath the surface of the water long enough to drown him.

The orca lives and hunts in packs each led by a dominant male. At sea it will chase, attack and eat almost anything that moves and represents a large enough meal, including fish, squid and seabirds. But it is especially fond of other marine mammals, most notably seals.

The sounds the killer whale makes — whistles, for communication with other members of its group; and clicks, for echolocation — produce a dramatic effect on animals within hearing range. Other dolphins and the smaller whales get away from the area as quickly as they can, and seals and penguins 'pop' from the water as they head frantically for the safety of land. And the orca has a voracious appetite: on examination, one dead specimen's stomach was found to contain the remains of 14 seals and 13 porpoises.

KORHAAN

Family Otididae

Among the more spectacular sights of the African veld is the courtship flight of the male redcrested korhaan, a medium-sized bird of the region's drier areas. He spends much of his time on the ground, well hidden among the low scrubland vegetation, but becomes a real show-off when he spots a potential bride.

To impress her, he clacks his bill loudly, utters a rising, whistle-like call and runs a short distance before taking off vertically, flying straight up for anything between ten and 30 metres. He then plunges down, tumbling over and over, his plumage fluffed out, opening his wings at the last moment to glide elegantly to a resting spot.

The korhaans are members of the bustard family. Eleven species occur in the region, six of which are endemic (that is, their ranges lie solely within the region) and one, the kori bustard, has the distinction of being the world's largest flying bird (see also below). Its great booming call fills the dawn air of the dry regions of southern Africa during the breeding season. It too gives quite a performance when courting, striding about importantly with neck puffed, tail fanned and wings planed and pointing down towards the ground.

start. Its flight is cumbersome, but powerful. Kori bustards, which are related to the korhaans (see opposite page), are found in the drier western parts of southern Africa, have greyish-brown plumage, long necks and a distinctive little crest behind their heads. They spend much of their time on the ground, walking sedately about in quest of rodents, insects, seeds, and even acacia gum (hence its Afrikaans name 'gompou') .

The female kori bustard is much smaller than the male. The latter, as mentioned, shows off abominably when out courting, strutting about in his fan-tailed finery, like an aspirant peacock, with wings and neck much in evidence.

KORI BUSTARD

Ardeotis kori

This is arguably the world's largest flying bird: the adult male weighs up to 19 kilograms and measures 1,35 metres from head to tail.

Not surprisingly, it takes to the air with difficulty, usually running through the veld to work up enough speed for take-off. It is also able, though, to lift itself from a standing

LAMMERGEIER (BEARDED VULTURE)

Gypaetus barbatus

This splendid bird of prey, which lives in the lofty mountains of the east, has a unique way of dealing with bones that are too large to swallow. It carries them high into the air and drops them down onto the rocks far below – and will continue to do so until they have been smashed into swallowable pieces (which may be up to 25 centimetres long).

K

Otherwise, or more correctly, known as the bearded vulture, the species is rare in southern Africa, confined mainly to the Drakensberg range and Lesotho's towering Maluti mountains. It has a huge wingspan (2,5 metres from tip to tip); builds its nest – of sticks lined with grass, bones, rags, hair and other bits and pieces – on a high ledge, to which it returns to breed each year.

These birds are classed as vultures, not because they look the part (though they are related to the latter) – indeed they are truly regal in size and appearance, and in the swift, agile way they hunt – but because they feed for the most part on the bones of carcasses and, to a lesser extent, on small mammals and the lambs of antelope.

LEGUAANS
Family Varanidae

More correctly known as monitors, these are the largest of southern Africa's, indeed the world's, present-day lizards: the Komodo monitor or 'dragon' (*Varanidae komodoensis*), discovered on the Lesser Sunda Islands east of Java only in 1912, reaches about three metres in length and preys on deer, pigs and other mammals.

More familiar is the water-leguaan or Nile monitor (*V. niloticus*), biggest of the African lizards,

which is a common resident of river valleys and an excellent swimmer which uses its long, powerful tail for propulsion. Its forked tongue, in snake-like fashion, serves as a sensor. It lives on crabs, mussels, fish, frogs, birds and crocodile eggs. Adults are about two metres long, and greyish-brown or dirty-olive in colour; the youngsters are exquisitely patterned in black and yellow.

The rock or white-throated leguaan (*V. albigularis*), southern Africa's only other monitor, is slightly smaller and found in open savanna semi-desert country. Its former scientific name, *V. exanthematicus*, refers to the bumps, bubicles and other irregularities on its body, which are especially prominent around its eyes, nostrils and joints ('exanthema' is Greek for a skin eruption).

Both these lizards can inflict severe bites, and cause considerable damage by lashing their tails, when threatened. The rock monitor's bite is especially frightening: once it gets a grip, it will hold on like a pit-bull terrier. It also defends itself by shamming death (though it continues to keep a wary eye on proceedings).

LEOPARD
Panthera pardus

This beautiful cat is the arch-survivor of the animal kingdom: tough, resilient and remarkably versatile, able to adapt to pretty well any kind of environment. It is found everywhere from the southern tip of Africa right up the continent and across to the eastern parts of Asia, its habitats varying from high mountain to coastal plain and from desert to lush equatorial rainforest.

It is also the only large carnivore to sustain a presence outside game parks and other protected areas, though in southern Africa its numbers have been drastically reduced by urban sprawl and, in the great interior, by commercial farming. Nevertheless it has remained elusive and wily enough to sidestep human society, though now and again it turns up in some pretty unlikely places – on the outskirts of such large centres as Johannesburg and Bloemfontein, for instance, and even in the gardens of some rural homesteads and the precincts of park rest-camps.

Secrets of survival

The leopard's spots – typically, dark rosettes on a tawny-yellow body – are vital to its wellbeing. They merge into the foliage of the tree in which it is resting, and blend extremely well with the more exposed shrub- and grasslands (indeed they are not dissimilar to the patterns of a modern soldier's uniform, which has been scientifically designed to provide optimum camouflage in the field). Just how important the markings are to the animal is evident from the way they have been adapted to suit each of its many habitats: the overall colour ranges from near-white through yellow and brown to almost pure black.

But the chief reason for the cat's uncanny resilience is its varied diet: it will hunt and eat almost any creature from the tiny mouse up to a giraffe calf, from insect to fish (some leopards are expert fishermen), and is not

L

averse to feeding on the rotting carcass of someone else's kill. It is therefore able to survive almost anywhere.

The hunt and kill

Given a choice, however, the leopard favours small to medium-sized antelope, which it catches mainly by stealth. It will often haul its kill up into a tree — a masterly stratagem for keeping its meal safe from marauding hyaenas, and from the vultures wheeling in the sky above (the birds cannot see through the canopy and, in any case, do not perch to feed). Essentially, though, it is not an arboreal species: it spends most of its time on *terra firma*, only taking to trees to escape its predators (notably lions), to cache its food, and occasionally also to relax.

Leopard lifestyle

For the rest, the leopard is very much a creature of the night. Males and females live apart; the male, which is much the larger of the two, has an extensive territory that usually overlaps with those of several females. Its mate usually gives birth to between one and three cubs, which she hides away in holes or dense thickets while she goes off hunting, moving to a new natal lair every two days or so. The cubs begin to accompany her on hunting expeditions when they are nine months old, and make their first kill (perhaps an impala lamb or baby scrub hare) two months later. When her offspring are about a year old the

mother becomes restless, increasingly impatient with and even aggressive towards them: she is almost ready to produce a new family and they are in the way. She then comes into oestrus, sets off on her own, scent-marking and calling. The male of the territory will respond and the two will mate, after which the youngsters are firmly, indeed unceremoniously, evicted and must fend for themselves.

LION

Panthera leo

Largest of African predators, the most social of the big cats, lord of the veld and universally respected for its physical power and ferocity, the lion has no natural enemies (except humankind). The male, in his regal fashion, tends towards indolence but his strength is awesome: he can break the neck of a full-grown wildebeest with one swipe of his massive paw. He is also able to show an impressive turn of speed, covering 100 metres in just four to six seconds.

It's rather surprising, therefore, that the death rate among the prides should be so high. The heaviest toll is taken by starvation among the cubs during droughts and other times of scarcity, and by parasite-borne diseases that attack the young when they are in poor condition. The latter fall victim, too, to adult aggression:

when a new male claims his mating rights, he often kills the offspring of his predecessor.

Moreover, adults are prone to injury during the hunt – from the horns of a buffalo, for example, or the lethal kick of a giraffe. Death also results, occasionally, from too-familiar contact with the humble porcupine (relished for the high fat content of its flesh), whose needle-sharp quills may pierce the cat's hide to set up an infection that spreads slowly, weakening the animal until it can no longer hunt for food.

Pride patterns

Lions live in prides of anything up to 30 members, the size dictated by the region and its bounty of food. Each group, though, is underpinned by a fairly permanent core of related females and their offspring, together

with an alliance (or 'coalition') of two or more adult males. Sometimes a single male will hold tenure. When they reach maturity, young females either stay with the natal pride or move off in a group to form a new one. Young males, on the other hand, always leave, wandering the veld in coalitions, usually with their brothers, until they are old enough and also strong enough to take over an existing pride. To do this they must drive out the incumbent males – often a bloody and sometimes even a fatal confrontation.

Once in control of the pride the victorious newcomers will live in harmony with each other. They do not compete for female favours, certainly not in any violent fashion: first-come, first-served is the guiding maxim, and once one of them has mated his dominance is generally accepted. All of which makes sense in the context of group survival: after all, the new males are brothers, and it doesn't really matter which of them becomes the sire, for the family genes will still pass to the new generation.

And here again, lions set records for physical prowess: while the female is receptive (the oestrus period lasts about five days) she will mate once every 20 minutes or so – a remarkable exhibition of sexual stamina. Often all the pride's females will come into oestrus at the same time, a synchronization designed by nature to keep the males busy: if only one lioness was available, the suitors would fight each other for the mating rights, and the injuries inflicted would weaken the pride.

The food chain

The hunt is a co-operative and subtle affair in which the females usually play the lead role, one lying in ambush while the others drive the prey towards her, perhaps first stampeding the herd to single out the weakest of its members. By co-operating, a pride can often catch and kill more than one animal (in one recorded attack, an astonishing seven wildebeest were brought down). Weight of numbers also lessens the chances of serious injury, a very real risk to a lone lion doing battle with, say, a big, sharp-horned buffalo. It was once thought that co-operative hunting also increased the actual amount of food available to each member of the pride, but this is probably not so. What it does do, though, is enable the group to protect the carcass from such tough and determined scavengers as vultures and hyaenas.

Meanwhile, the lordly males watch the action from the sidelines and, when the chase-and-kill is over, move in to claim the choicest parts.

The cubs are sometimes last in the food queue, which may offend human sensibilities but, again, this is simply nature's way of ensuring continuity, for only healthy adults can produce the new generations that will enable the pride, and ultimately the species, to survive.

LOCUSTS
Family Acrididae

Of all living things that inhabit or visit the southern African countryside, the locust is without doubt the least welcome: a swarm on the move advances relentlessly on a front of up to eight kilometres, can be 60 kilometres long and will, in a single 24-hour period, consume enough food to fill nearly two million people.

In its wake it leaves a land stripped of every vestige of greenery.

North African locusts – the eighth of the biblical Plagues of Egypt – are even more monstrous: a single desert swarm can cover 1 000 square kilometres, and its 50 billion close-packed individuals will darken the noon-day sky to blackness.

Locusts, which differ from ordinary grasshoppers only in their habit of swarming, can and do live solitary lives, but when weather and food conditions are just right for breeding they begin to congregate, the population explodes, and soon great armies of brightly coloured nymphs, or hoppers (wingless juveniles) are marching across the land. As the hoppers mature, so they take off *en masse* to migrate, resting up during the heat of the day and feeding in the cooler hours. In due course the swarm will settle and, if conditions are still favourable, mate and lay eggs to produce a new generation, so continuing the cycle of destruction.

Africa is host to four species, one of which – the brown locust (*Locustana pardalina*) – is permanently resident in South Africa, menacing the pastures and wheat and maize farms of the Karoo and western Free State. More troublesome, though, is the red locust (*Nomadacris septemfasciata*), which occasionally wreaks havoc among the sugar plantations of KwaZulu-Natal. Now and again, after good rains, a subspecies of the desert locust, *Schistocerca gregaria*, makes it appearance in the northern regions. So too, but very infrequently, does the West African tropical species *Locusta migratoria*.

A great deal of money and effort is invested in locust control. Careful and continuous watch is kept on potential swarms, which are then sprayed with chemicals both from the air and by eradication teams on the ground.

LUNGFISH

Protopterus annectens

This weird creature, found in swamps, floodplains and pans from the Kruger National Park north to the Zambesi River (as well as in South America), provides a glimpse of the immensely ancient past – to the time when life forms began to forsake the shrinking rivers and lakes of the Gondwanaland super-continent to make a fragile home on land. Remains of these fish, dated to 150 million years ago, have been found in the Great Karoo.

This 'living fossil' has a rudimentary lung consisting of an air sac, which enables it to breathe during the winter months, when its watery surrounds dry up. It survives the long droughts by retiring to, and hibernating in, a cocoon of hard clay. It breeds on the edges of the swamps, where the male constructs a crude nest in the rotting vegetation.

L

Lungfish are virtually blind, able to respond only to light and dark. To compensate for this, though, they are extremely sensitive to smells, and to pressure and vibration – like most fish they have a 'lateral line' that detects the movement of other creatures in the water. But they also have long, spindle-like fins that help them get about on the ground, using the fins not for propulsion but to feel their way around, in much the same way a blind person uses a white stick.

MAMBAS
Genus *Dendroaspis*

The black mamba, which grows to more than four metres in length, ranks among Africa's most dangerous snakes: when cornered it will rear up, open its mouth wide and emit a hollow-sounding hiss before striking. If you meet it in the wild, you're best advised to step back smartly, at which point it will (usually) retreat into the undergrowth.

This snake's bite is extremely poisonous: its fangs, which are positioned at the front of its mouth, carry up to 400 milligrams of venom, toxin that attacks the body's nerves and heart, and just 15 milligrams of which can prove fatal in humans if not quickly treated with an antidote. The victim, though sometimes remaining fully conscious, becomes paralyzed and will in due course die

of respiratory failure. The black mamba – which is in fact dark grey to olive-brown in colour – lives in the fairly open, lower-lying countryside of the subcontinent among rocks or in holes (it is especially fond of termite nests). It feeds on warm-blooded prey such as rodents and dassies.

The green mamba is, as its name suggests, bright green in colour and, although shyer than its black cousin and less venomous, its bite is also dangerous, occasionally fatal. It is an inhabitant of the forests and coastal bush of Africa's eastern parts.

MEERKAT
Suricata Suricatta

The most sociable and, to human eyes, perhaps the most delightful of all mammals is the suricate, commonly known as the meerkat: a bright-eyed, pixie-faced, alert, inquisitive little creature that until recently belonged, with the mongooses, to the viverrid group. Both now belong to the family Herpestidae. The public hardly knew of the animal's existence until a few years ago, when a research study, followed by a television documentary, soon led to a starring role in a major Disney film.

Meerkats are carnivores, but they find themselves in the awkward position of being both predator and prey – a problem they have solved in quite remarkable fashion.

The key to their success is co-operation. Meerkats live in bands of up to 30 individuals, and spend their days digging furiously for insects, grubs, geckos, scorpions and the like, which means that, for much of the time, their heads are buried in sand or earth. This preoccupation makes them highly vulnerable to both the high-flying eagle and the ground-living predators such as jackals.

So the meerkat has evolved an elaborate and most effective early-warning system. Or rather, two complementary systems.

Two lines of defence

First, each member of the group stops foraging every few seconds to sit bolt upright, on its hindlegs, to peer up at the sky and sur-vey the surround-ings for the slightest sign of danger, and will sound the alarm when it sees or sus-pects a threat.

However, the meerkats will give their undi-vided attention to the search for food when the second system gears in. This involves the posting of a 'profes-sional guard', a full-time sen-tinel who stops

work completely to sit, with head erect and front paws held out, on a termite mound, tree stump or some other convenient vantage point to scan the area. Throughout its tour of duty the sentry makes a soft, regular chirping sound that signals all is well. If the noise ceases, the others will know something is wrong. If it spots a predator, on the other hand, it will give either a short bark, which means there's a bird of prey around, or a higher pitched sound, which identifies a terrestrial threat, where-upon the whole group flees to the nearest available shelter.

A group of foraging meerkats will post a full-time sentry to scan land and sky for signs of danger.

Occasionally, though, predators do manage to get close, even with a sentry in place, and sometimes there's no cover nearby. A snake, per-haps, will venture onto the scene, and on these occasions the meerkats will crowd together, rock backwards and forwards, their fur raised and their mouths agape, and then launch themselves in a sin-gle, sinuous, writhing mass at the intruder. The latter invariably backs off.

M

Acting in concert

The co-operative approach extends further – to, for instance, parenting. When the dominant female gives birth, one of her junior relatives stays behind in the burrow to look after the offspring – a vital task in a world full of danger – while the rest of the group venture forth. The mother goes out with them and is allowed to forage without interruption – she is excused sentry duty – in order to build up her milk supplies.

Although meerkats are marvellously co-operative within their own groups, they treat neighbouring ones with unbridled hostility. They are highly terrestrial little animals, and when another band approaches they again bunch up to leap about in a kind of war dance, posturing and kicking up the dust in a display of collective strength. They then mount a frontal assault. The larger group nearly always wins the battle, celebrates with a great show of mutual congratulation and occasionally, in all too human fashion, attracts deserters from the routed enemy.

MOLE-RAT

Cryptomys damarensis

The Damaraland mole-rat is a mammal, but a very strange one: its lifestyle resembles nothing so much as that of the social insects. Like the ants, the bees and the termites and quite unlike any other mammal, it lives in underground colonies (of up to 40 individuals), each with its queen, its workers and its elite minority of sturdy soldiers.

Only the queen mole-rat breeds and, to fulfill her regal role, makes sure that the other, smaller females are unable to do so: the follicles remain undeveloped and they are not receptive to mating. On the death of the queen, though, several of them suddenly begin putting on weight. In due course one of them succeeds to the throne; the others disperse to find unrelated males.

Unlike other 'eusocial' species, the mole-rats do not leave the group in order to found new colonies (unless the queen dies). This may seem surprising when one considers how powerful the reproductive urge is throughout the natural world, but in this animal's desert environment — its major home is the Kalahari — there are even stronger imperatives.

The molerat's lifestyle is very much like that of the social insects.

Food is scarce for all the desert's life forms, and the mole-rat faces special difficulties: virtually blind but armed with long, chisel-like incisors and a sturdy body, it burrows for bulbs beneath the surface of the sandveld in random fashion. In this dark world eyesight is useless, food is found by chance, and the colony needs to keep up its numbers if it is to locate enough to eat to survive as a viable group. In short, it simply cannot afford to lose members through dispersal while the queen is still reigning.

Mole-rats are remarkable diggers: one colony of 16 individuals is on record as having excavated almost a kilometre of burrows in just one month, throwing up 2,5 tonnes of sandy soil in the process.

MOSQUITOES
Family Culicidae

These tiny insects are responsible for more human deaths – from a range of diseases that include yellow fever and, more significantly, malaria and its complications – than all the rest of nature's creatures put together.

The culprits are the females of some of the *Anopheles* group, of which there are more than 200 species capable of transmitting malaria, only one or two of which account for the disease in southern Africa. Yellow fever is passed on by just one species of the genus *Aedes*.

The female needs blood in order to produce her young, and to do so she sinks her sharp proboscis into the skin, injecting an anti-clotting saliva while drawing out the free-flowing

Mosquitoes kill more people than all other creatures put together.

blood. If she is carrying the malaria or yellow fever parasite (picked up from the blood of a previous host), she will pass the infection on. The male is built quite differently: his jaws are weak, and he has to be content with the juice of plants.

The eggs can only develop in water, the larvae feeding on and eventually pupating in it. The process is rapid, for water quickly evaporates in the hot African sun. The eggs remain dormant during the long months of drought.

An effective vaccination against yellow fever has been developed, but the disease remains a threat in Africa and South and Central America.

Malaria is far more of a problem. Although under control through most of the subcontinent, more than a million people in the broader African region die of it each year, most of them children. Some strains are resistant to drugs. Among the most serious afflictions are complications of what is known as malignant tertian malaria. These include cerebral malaria (which affects the brain) and blackwater fever, a symptom of which is dark, reddish-black urine (red blood cells are destroyed, often leading to death from kidney failure).

M

OCTOPUSES AND SQUIDS

Cephalopods

These marine creatures are the most advanced of all invertebrates (animals without backbones), endowed with complex nervous systems, highly efficient sensory organs – and even the capacity to remember and learn from experience.

They belong to a group of molluscs (a group which also includes shells, clams and oysters) known as cephalopods, a collective name which refers to the way their 'legs', or tentacles, are joined to their heads.

Perhaps their most remarkable features are their eyes, which are very like those of a human's although the two life forms evolved quite independently of each other – a fact which promises interesting possibilities in man's search for extra-terrestrial life. The eye of octopus and man are structured and function in much the same way, though the cephalopod's has wider vision.

The eyes of some species, too, are extraordinarily large. Those of the giant squid *Architeuthis princeps*, a deep-sea monster that can reach an impressive 18 metres in length, are the size of footballs.

Among other ocean residents with especially keen eyesight are sharks (which adjust optical reception to changing light intensity in much the same way a cat does), dolphins, whales and, oddly enough, the humble scallop, some species of which have up to 200 'eyes' – tiny, light-sensitive blue dots – ranged along the sides of their shells.

Hunting patterns

Octopuses are common all the way along the southern African coast, lurking in lairs among the rocks (though some are found at enormous depths – 3 000 metres and more). Here they wait in ambush for passing crayfish, crabs and other crustaceans and molluscs, enveloping their prey with their eight sucker-studded tentacles. Once the victim is thus immobilized, the octopus cracks the shell open with its powerful, parrot-like beak. Most octopuses are rather smaller than is popularly supposed, though one Pacific Ocean species reaches nearly five metres in length.

For defence, the octopus relies on speed – it swims away quickly by forcing jets of water through a tunnel in its mantle – and on a 'smoke-screen' of ink it discharges from a special sac in its body.

For their part, squids – which have ten tentacles as opposed to the octopus's eight – normally swim with the aid of fins, but in emergencies they too will use jet propulsion and a cloud of ejected black ink to make good their escape.

Octopuses and squids are generally harmless to man, though most can deliver a nasty bite and one little species, the blue-ringed octopus that lives in the oceans around Australia, has a bite that can lead to death. It preys on crabs, which it catches by ejecting a paralysing poison into the surrounding water.

OOGPISTER

Anthia species

This meat-eating beetle, whose Afrikaans name translates (approximately and politely) as the 'eye-squirter', uses a highly effective weapon when it feels threatened: it ejects a hot, pungent organic acid that can blind a bird or a small mammal – and cause a lot of discomfort to a human who gets too close. The insect has a black body girdled by a white stripe – a warning signal to would-be attackers.

There is nothing especially un-usual about the oogpister's defence strategy. Plenty of other life forms – insects, plants, animals like the honey badger and the polecat – use chemical weapons to protect themselves, though admittedly this particular creature's technique is rather more dramatic than most. The majority of the tenebrionid (dark-coloured) beetles, for instance, secrete unpleasant and sometimes poisonous fluids over themselves.

But what *is* remarkable about the oogpister's defence mechanism is the evolutionary response it has triggered in an entirely different kind of species. The young Kalahari sand lizard (*Eremias lugubris*) is also black with a white stripe, and has evolved a stiff-legged, arched-back gait that bears more than a passing resemblance to the way the beetle walks.

The similarity is effective enough to confuse a predator, make it think twice about its 'poisonous' victim for a second or two – long enough for the lizard to scuttle away to safety. As the little reptile grows older it develops other means of defence, taking on a duller colour and moving about in more lizard-like fashion.

For defence, the young sand lizard takes on the colouring, and the gait, of the poisonous oogpister.

OSTRICH
Struthio camelus

The ostrich is the largest of the world's birds: the male stands nearly 2,5 metres tall.

This is the largest of the world's birds: the male stands nearly 2,5 metres tall, and is too heavy to take to the air, or to build a nest in a tree. It is also unusual in the way it mates and looks after its eggs and offspring.

The male will mate with as many females as he's able to, but reserves his special loyalty for just one, the 'major hen', with whom he forms a close bond. The two create a nest (which is no more than a shallow scrape in open ground), and there the females – up to 18 of them – lay their eggs. But only the male and his partner perform the incubation duties, he during the night, she during the day.

However, the pile of eggs often grows to an unmanageable number and, when this happens, she ejects the surplus ones – those laid by the other females, which occupy the outer fringes of the pile. These litter the ground around the nest and act as decoys, diverting an intruder's attention away from her own eggs.

Speed and deception

The ostrich's chief means of defence is speed – the bird's long, powerful legs can carry it along at up to 60 km/h – but it is not its only one. Like the meerkat (page 70), it is very keen of eye and tends to gather with others when feeding, and one member of the group is always on the lookout for danger. The birds also mix with herds of larger mammals such as zebra and wildebeest, so collective vigilance is enhanced even further.

And then there is camouflage. The male ostrich's black and white plumage hardly seems to provide the best form of deception but, surprisingly, the colouring is highly effective in the heat of the day, when the air is shimmering in the rising currents: from a distance, a flock of ostriches looks uncannily like a patch of rounded bushes.

Fortunes from feathers

At one period, during late Victorian and Edwardians times, ostrich feathers were in huge demand in the world of fashion and a lucrative ostrich farming industry grew up around the Little Karoo town of Oudtshoorn. At the height of the boom, in 1913, more than 450 000 kilograms of feathers were being exported each year. The industry then slumped, but modern tanning techniques have led to something of a revival – the skins are used for high-fashion leather goods, wallets, handbags, shoes, belts; the eggshells for painted lampshades and ornaments;

the tail feathers now adorn household dusters instead of stylish necks; ostrich steaks and biltong have become culinary delicacies. And the eggs, each weighing more than a kilogram, are enormously nutritious: in omelette terms, a single one is equal to 24 hen's eggs.

OWLS
Families Tytonidae and Strigidae

Most owls are renowned for their excellent night vision, but some species depend even more on their incredibly acute hearing. The barn owl (*Tyto alba*), for example, can discern the tiniest of sounds made by the mice and other rodents it hunts, and is able to locate its source with uncanny accuracy.

Once it has pinpointed its prey, the owl will noiselessly swoop in for the kill, lining up its talons on and following the scurrying mouse through every twist and turn, even on the darkest of nights. It can do this because it has two receptors – small depressions to either side of its beak which, together with the facial disk, concentrate the sound waves that reach its ears – and because its ears are unevenly positioned, the right one a little higher than the left. This asymmetrical arrangement enables it to compare a noise at slightly different levels and to lock in on its precise position.

Masters of disguise

Twelve species of owl are found in southern Africa, the largest of them the giant eagle owl (*Bubo lacteus*), which is found in the northern parts of the region. Most of them are accomplished masters of deceit – which they have to be since, otherwise, they would be highly vulnerable to predators and harassment by other birds in the revealing light of day.

The feathers at the back of the pearlspotted owl's head, for instance, are patterned in the form of a 'face' so that it looks as though the bird is ever-watchful and always fully aware of potential attackers (some butterflies also display bogus eyes, huge ones that stare angrily from the surface of their wings). The feathers of the tiny scops owl, which roosts on the stem of a shade tree during the day, blend quite exquisitely with the bark. To reinforce the deception, the owl changes its distinctive outline by elongating both its body and ear-tufts, and hides its very recognizable eyes by reducing them to mere slits.

The whitefaced owl also stretches its body and closes its eyes to change its all-too-familiar physical character – and uses yet another ploy when actually threatened. It fluffs its feathers out, with wings extended and eyes wide open, to appear a lot bigger and fiercer that it really is.

OXPECKERS
Family Buphagidae

These enterprising birds make their homes, not in the trees and bushes of the veld but on the hide of one or other of the bigger grazing animals, creating a kind of mobile dining table on which they spend most of their lives.

The oxpecker (which is related to the starling) clings firmly to the back or side of the beast with its strong, sharp claws, feeding on the ticks and other small, unwelcome creatures that plague the large herbivores of the veld. The relationship, curious though it might seem at first glance, makes a lot of sense: the bird enjoys a constant food supply, and the animal has the benefit of a built-in vacuum cleaner.

For the mammal, though, the association has its downside. Prising off a tick can open up a small running sore, which the bird will peck away at for weeks, initially for the flies it attracts and then for the maggots, and over time the suppurating wound will weaken the animal. The oxpecker also uses its unusual larder as a firm platform on which to rest, and to go through the courting and mating rituals – though it leaves it at breeding time to nest in a hole high in the trees. Often, it will construct its nest from hair taken from the hide of the host animal.

Southern Africa is home to the world's only two oxpecker species: the yellowbilled and redbilled, both found in the northern regions. They are most often seen in game reserves – modern cattle-dipping methods have more or less forced them out of the farmlands.

OYSTERS
Genus *Ostrea*

These bivalved (two-shelled) molluscs bring delight to food connoisseurs the world over, especially when washed down with a bottle of good bubbly. But they also hold considerable interest for the biologist, not least for the ways different species reproduce themselves

Broadly speaking there are two groups of oysters: those who change their sex from time to time (hermaphrodites, who may be males one year and females the next) and those who remain the same sex throughout their lives.

When summer begins to warm the sea, those members of the first group who find themselves male will release sperm that is carried by the currents to the females, who will fertilize and incubate the eggs until they hatch. A single female will routinely produce more than a million eggs in a season (a fertility rate that is probably the basis of the oyster's reputed aphrodisiac properties). Those in the second group release their eggs into water, where they are fertilized, and they pass through the hatching and larval stages without any input from the female.

The oyster's soft body is enclosed with two heavy, hinged, very irregular shells which are kept tightly closed by a strong muscle. Baby oysters go through a brief free swimming stage before they look for a smooth rock surface to which they can attach themselves (this they do with the lower, bigger valve, or shell). Once firmly in place, they will stay in the same position for up to 25 years.

Oysters, of course, are famed (and cultivated) for the valuable pearls they produce. These are simply accumulations of the shiny material known as mother-of-pearl, a layer of which coats the inside of the shell and is periodically covered by a fresh layer. When foreign matter – a grain of sand, for example – gets lodged inside the oyster, it too is progressively covered in layers of mother-of-pearl to produce a shiny sphere.

Signposts to glittering fortune

In southern Africa, curiously enough, oysters have played their part in the production of another precious stone – the diamond. When the diamond fields of South Africa's West Coast were discovered in the 1920s, the prospectors who flocked to the area found that their search was made easier by a curious scientific phenomenon: the gems occurred in sandy soil containing fossils of an extinct species of warm-water oyster (*Ostea prismatica*). The two elements – diamonds and shellfish – have nothing in common, but both were linked to some major geological upheaval that, in the distant past, had changed the ocean's currents, killing the oysters and sweeping the diamonds ashore. The 'oyster line' was profitably used by the first diggers as a beacon to the fabulous wealth that lay beneath the ancient beach gravels.

PANGOLIN
Manis temminckii

One of the weirdest of southern Africa's mammals is the pangolin: ancient in origin, it is unique among the region's animals in that it is covered not by hair, but by rows of tough, razor-edged, plate-like scales.

This formidable coat of armour has helped to protect the species from its enemies for the past 40 million years or so. It is not, though, the pangolin's only means of defence. At the merest hint of a threat this little tank-like creature freezes, and in open, stony places can easily be mistaken for a rock.

If detected, it will roll itself up into a tight ball, covering its face and soft belly. Any attempt to unroll it provokes a vicious scything motion of its tail, whose scales will lacerate its persecutor's snout and paws.

And there is a third and often conclusive deterrent: if eaten, it will inflict severe damage on the predator's stomach. It is thought that large carnivores, such as lions, may sometimes die from torn guts after swallowing one of these animals.

Large animals, such as lions, may die from torn guts after swallowing a pangolin.

The pangolin is a solitary creature which feeds, mainly at night, on ants and termites. It locates these by smell and digs into their tunnels with its front claws. It then inserts its long (25-centimetre), rod-like tongue, which is covered in sticky saliva and acts rather like fly-paper, into the tunnels to draw out the insects.

PERIPATUS
Genus *Peripatopsis*

This is one of Nature's strangest creatures. Immensely ancient in origin, it is thought to have been the far-distant link between the arthropod invertebrates – a group that includes the insects, spiders, centipedes and lobsters – and modern worms. In general appearance it resembles a velvety caterpillar.

The peripatus's respiratory system and clawed legs (anything from 16 to 23 pairs) are similar to those of the insects, its internal structure to that of the worms. More specifically, the simple eye, the blood system and the paired kidneys are worm-like. For defence, it ejects a sticky slime that can entangle an enemy, or immobilize one of the insects that the peripatus eats.

Most notable of Africa's 13 different species is the velvety, caterpillar-like *Peripatopsis capensis*. Limited to cool, humid environments, all live in the temperate rain forests and caves of the south.

In the cradle of life
The peripatus has remained virtually unchanged in form and habit for at least 500 million years. It was certainly alive and well in the Cambrian epoch, when, as scientist R.F. Lawrence writes, 'it could be truly said that the earth was still "without form and void". All life existed only in the

sea, and the bare, denuded earth was as yet without the softening effects of plant life. The shores of the ancient seas, the fruitful and teeming region between the tidal levels, are thought to have been the cradle of all life, and here the early ancestor of Peripatus may have lived, using its sturdy legs to walk upon firm ground, perhaps the first of all animals to emerge from the sea and set upon the conquest of land'.

POISONOUS PLANTS

The lovely oleander (*Nerium oleander*) is highly toxic to both animals and man. Indeed, the use of its branches – for example, as meat-skewers and cooking-pot stirrers – can cause death. Even the smoke from a burning oleander is dangerous, as may be the honey made from its flowers.

The plant, a native of the southern Mediterranean regions, graced South African gardens with relatively little harm done for close on 150 years but then, in the 1940s, it began to spread, to invade parts of the western and southern Cape in earnest and, in particular, to overwhelm riverine vegetation. It remains a real pest on stock farms.

The oleander is one of many toxic species, both local and imported, that plague domestic gardens and the country areas alike. Some look innocuous, even appealing; others have rather attractive common names, conjuring images that belie, often tragically, their lethal nature. Among the most dangerous are:

❏ Mushrooms. The death-cap mushroom (*Amanita phalloides*) is a fungus that, even when eaten in tiny quantities, can be fatal. The symptoms – unbearable thirst, intense stomach pains, vomiting and diarrhoea – begin two days after ingestion, will probably disappear for a while but then return to push the victim into a coma. Other species to avoid include the fly agaric mushroom (*Amanita muscaria*), quicker acting but rather less hazardous unless eaten in quantity.

❏ The common and most pleasing, lilac-flowered syringa tree (*Melia azedarach*). Both its leaves and fruit are toxic.

❏ Many members of the large Eurphorbia family, whose often milky sap (latex) can blister the skin and, if in contact with the eyes, may cause blindness.

❏ The castor oil plant (*Ricinus communis*), a familiar southern African invader species (originally from tropical Africa) whose seeds look like beans but which are highly toxic. Among the symptoms is severe stomach upset, occasionally (especially if the victim is a child) ending in death. The species is common in riverine and disturbed areas.

❏ The pretty, pink-bloomed March lily (*Amaryllis belladonna*), indigenous to the Western Cape.

- The well-known tamboti tree (*Spirostachys africana*), which is similar to the oleander (see above) in its action and effect. Its poison can be transmitted by smoke, so never use the wood for barbecues.
- The various small tree species that belong to the *Acokanthera* genus, known as Bushman's poison plants. The San hunters once tipped their arrows with the sap.

POLECAT

Ictonyx striatus

This little black-and-white animal, southern Africa's only polecat species, defends itself in rather unusual fashion. Its main weapon: an indescribably foul smell.

The polecat's first reaction to danger, though, is to stand firm and fluff out the hairs of its body and tail so that it appears to be much larger and more dangerous than it really is. Unhappily, when it finds itself on a road it tends to threaten oncoming cars in the same fashion, and dies a quick and messy death.

However, the technique is often surprisingly successful in the bush, deterring predators as large as brown hyaenas. It is especially effective when the animal activates its second defensive mechanism: it lifts its tail and, from its anal glands, ejects a miasmic protective odour. The smell is persistent, lingering for hours.

In appearance the striped polecat is much like but rather larger than the striped weasel. It has four white bands along its black back, white patches between eyes and ears, a white spot on its forehead and a long, bushy tail. It feeds on insects, rodents, snakes, lizards and other small creatures — and on birds' eggs.

The animal is harmless enough but is nevertheless persecuted by suspicious farmers, who regard it as a poultry thief. An even bigger threat to its survival, perhaps, is the domestic dog, whose numbers in the rural areas are increasing as the human population expands. Not only will the dogs hunt it, but compete with it for the limited food resources.

PORCUPINE

Hystrix africaeaustralis

This is the largest of southern Africa's rodents, and perhaps the best-armed of all the smaller mammals: its back is covered in a crest of needle-sharp quills which, contrary to popular belief, the porcupine cannot 'shoot'. It does, though, use them most effectively, and sometimes lethally, in other ways.

This defensive system is all too frequently put to the test, for the porcupine is especially favoured by the larger carnivores, probably because its flesh has an unusually high fat content. It responds to a threat by presenting its rear end or side to the attacker, bristling ferociously and rattling the special hollow quills on its tail. With its crest erect, it is able to appear almost double its real size (the animal can weigh an impressive 24 kilograms).

The porcupine may also run backwards against its enemy. When it does, its quills easily become dislodged and pierce the predator, causing severe pain and, occasionally, a fatal infection (though, again, the belief that the quills are either barbed or poisonous is quite mistaken). Surprisingly, wounds from too-close encounters with porcupines are a major cause of death among lions: the infection weakens the great cat so that it can no longer compete for food, and it eventually dies of starvation (see page 67).

Porcupines are monogamous, generally solitary creatures certainly when out foraging, hiding in burrows during the day and feeding on vegetable matter at night. Farmers tend to dislike them because they are partial to such root crops as potatoes and pumpkins.

PORT JACKSON WILLOW

Acacia saligna

Of all the alien invader plants that have found a happy home in southern Africa, the Port Jackson willow has perhaps proved the most damaging to the environment.

The species, an ultra-tough perennial shrub or small tree of the large *Acacia* genus, was introduced from Australia in the mid-1840s to help stabilize the windblown sands of the Cape Flats, the low-lying area that separates Cape Town and the Peninsula from the lush winelands of the hinterland. At that time it was a nightmare of drifting dunes known to the Dutch as 'Die Groote Woeste Vlakte' (The Great Desolate Plain).

The plants did their work well enough – in fact, too well: they adapted easily to their new habitat and, lacking the natural checks of their homeland, spread virulently to pose a real threat to the Cape's indigenous flora.

In a kind of tit-for-tat development, the Cape bietou bush or bush-tick berry (*Chrysanthemoides monilifera*), accidentally introduced to Australia in 1908 – in ships' ballast – multiplied alarmingly in that country, endangering the natural vegetation of the coastal areas, damaging beach-planting programmes and blocking access to beaches.

P

PORTUGUESE MAN O' WAR

Physalia

Also called the bluebottle, this troublesome little marine organism, a close relative of the jellyfish, is well known to and feared by most bathers, especially those enjoying the balmy waters of the eastern seaboard.

Like several other marine life forms, bluebottles live on the surface (as a group they are known as nekton), travelling on the winds and currents of the world's oceans.

The bluebottle is a simple creature, its structure consisting of a blue balloon-like float from which long strands of poisonous tentacles trail. These tentacles inflict extremely painful stings, which produce inflamed welts on the skin and, very occasionally (if the victim has an allergy), cause death. They can sting even when washed up on the beach.

The extraordinary thing about the bluebottle, however, is that it is a communal, not an individual entity. The balloon, which serves as both a float and a sail, is simply a semi-transparent, sky-blue, air-filled membrane produced collectively by and attached to various, genetically quite different organisms.

This collection of larval and adult animals form a tangled mass (largely composed of the original polyp and its progeny) at the side of the balloon, and from it trail the enormously long tendrils. Each 'colonist' has its function: some provide the sensory organs, others are defensive, still others take in and digest food, a few are sexual specialists. There is no central nervous system – instead, messages essential to survival are conducted through the 'body' by means of electrical impulses.

And the instructions are very clear: the bluebottle is, among other things, a very efficient seafarer, able to set and change course, and expand and trim its sail by adjusting its curvature to the sea-breeze. And, if it's becalmed beneath a too-hot sun, it will deflate the balloon and keep it moist by rolling.

PRAYING MANTIS

Family Mantidae

This strange insect is known for its eerily humanoid appearance – in classic pose, it looks like nothing so much as a gaunt old man, motionless, lost in prayer.

The mantis, a carnivorous creature, has long front legs armed with spikes which secure its living prey, and which are often held together. Its two large compound eyes and three simple eyes are set in a triangular-shaped head which, uniquely, it can swivel in all directions.

However, the mantis can also (and usually does) imitate a leaf or stem:

its elongated body and green-brown colouring provides perfect camouflage. The males are invariably winged, though many of the females are not. Females have special glands

which secrete a kind of foam to protect their eggs, and during mating, with callous aplomb, they often eat their partner.

The mantis is the object of profound superstition in some parts of rural southern Africa.

PROTEAS
Family Proteaceae

Members of this large family of flowering plants are hugely varied in form: indeed they were named (by the great Swedish botanist Carl Linneaus) after Proteus, the mythological Greek god who could change his shape at will. Southern Africa is home to 14 different genera of Proteaceae and around 400 species, one of which was the very first of the region's plants to be recorded in a book – published in Antwerp in 1605 (though it was wrongly identified as a kind of daisy and given quite the wrong country of origin).

Most of the southern African species are to be found in the fynbos vegetation of the Cape Floristic Kingdom (see page 20). Those of the genus *Protea* itself (which has about 130 members) are distinguished by their needle-shaped flowers, which are grouped together to form one compact head surrounded by brightly coloured bracts, the whole looking very much like a single flower.

Among the best known species are the beautiful king protea (*Protea cynaroides*), South Africa's national flower, which has the largest flower head of all; the seven-metre waboom (or wagon-tree, *P. nitida*); the sugarbush (*P. repens*) and the mountain rose (*P. nana*), which is rather drab when viewed from above (it turns its face downwards) but, seen from below, as you climb up the hillside, translucently exquisite.

Other genera in the family include *Leucospermum*, whose 50 or so species are popularly known as pincushions, and *Leucadendron*, among which is the silver tree (see page 96). One of the loveliest of proteas is the blushing bride (*Serruria florida*); among the rarest the marsh rose (*Orothamnus zeyheri*), found only around Hermanus and on the slopes of the Kogelberg in the Western Cape.

P

PYTHONS
Family Boidae

These huge snakes are remarkable not only for their size and the way they suffocate (not crush, as popularly supposed) their prey to death, but also for the manner in which some species both protect and incubate their eggs.

A female python will lay up to 100 eggs and coil herself around them, contracting her muscles in a series of 'shivers' to raise her body temperature in order to warm the clutch. She may also move the eggs in and out of the sunlight.

The African rock python (*Python sebae*), which does not in fact fit into this maternal pattern, is the continent's largest snake, growing to about 4,5 metres, sometimes longer (the record stands at more than nine metres) and reaches an average weight of 45 kilograms.

The snake is often found near water, in which – just like the crocodile – it will immerse itself for hours with only its eyes and nostrils protruding. It kills by coiling itself around the victim, which may sometimes be as large as a small antelope, and then swallowing it whole through specially hinged jaws. Its digestive juices can dissolve almost every part of the prey. It can also go for surprisingly long periods without food – captive specimens have been known to eat nothing whatsoever for more than two years.

Pythons are considered to be 'primitive' snakes in evolutionary terms because they have retained tiny remnants of a pelvis and claw-like hindlegs. In the past, they were hunted to the point of species endangerment for their beautifully marked skins, but are now strictly protected within the region.

The python can swallow a small antelope through its specially hinged jaws.

QUAGGA
Equus quagga

For long this horse-like animal was thought to be a separate species of zebra, but no-one could be quite sure because it was hunted to extinction during the 19th century. The last recorded specimen died in the Amsterdam zoo in 1883; in South Africa, it was last recorded in the wild as far back as 1878.

The quagga – so named for its harsh 'kwa-ha' bark – had a warm chocolate-brown coat and creamy-white legs, but only the head, neck and foreparts of the back bore stripes. Large herds once roamed the plains of what was then the Cape Colony and southern Orange Free State.

It certainly seemed to have been a distinct species, but in 1987 a series of DNA tests, on tissue taken from a stuffed museum animal, seemed to indicate that it may be merely a colour variant, and the southernmost subspecies, of the common Burchell's zebra. The classification issue, though, has by no means been resolved.

The research led to the Quagga experimental breeding programme, launched to 'rebreed' the animal from the Burchell's zebra specimens from KwaZulu-Natal and Etosha (Namibia), selected for their colouring and lack of stripes. Difficulties encountered, however, may be evidence that the animal was indeed a separate species.

RHINOCEROS
Family Rhinocerotidae

These massive mammals – an adult male white rhino weighs in at more than two tonnes – are a throwback to that far-distant age when mega-herbivores ruled the earth.

Rhinoceroses flourished in various forms in Africa, Europe, Asia and, in the Eocene epoch more than 60 million years ago, in North America, reaching their peak 20 million years later when some species grew to a height of more than five metres and a length of nearly ten metres.

Towards extinction
Today, rhinos are among the most endangered of the larger animals. Just three decades ago there were still 65 000 of the black species on the African continent; today, fewer than 3 000 remain, nearly all of them to be found in southern Africa (this is the fastest recorded decline of any large mammal in documented history). Its white cousin has fared better, but only marginally so.

Initially – from about a hundred years ago – the rhino populations suffered grievously from the expansion of human settlement and the resultant loss of habitat. More recently, though, they have been hunted to the brink of extinction for their meat, hides and, most especially, for their horns. Rhino horn is much sought after in the Far East as a fever

P

suppressant and antidote to poison (but not, contrary to popular belief, as a sexual stimulant) and in India and the Middle East for ornamentation. There are huge profits to be made from the illegal trade, and organized poaching is both rampant and ruthless. Moreover, these huge but harmless animals are pathetically vulnerable: they are short-sighted, easily located at their watering places, and can be approached from downwind without difficulty.

Black and white

The two species, though related, differ in size, temperament, feeding habits and in other ways.

The 'white' rhinoceros is in fact dark grey in colour; the name is thought to be a corruption of the Afrikaans word 'wyd', or wide, a reference to the square-lipped mouth of a grazing animal.

By contrast, the black rhino (again, the name is misleading, and applied only to distinguish it from its cousin) is a browser, its pointed mouth well adapted to its diet of leaves and branches. It is also the smaller and more aggressive of the two species, quite prepared to charge you, snorting and puffing its anger, if you intrude on its patch. It doesn't see too well, but has excellent senses of smell and hearing. Most such charges are bluffs but still, when you're walking in rhino country, keep close to the taller trees – and be prepared to climb them in a hurry.

The great rescue

Few conservation stories have had such a happy outcome as that of the white rhino (though the saga is not quite over yet). At one time – during the early 1900s – it seemed that the animal was doomed. But the southern subspecies, sustained in the Umfolozi area by the far-sighted conservationists of the Natal Parks Board, survived and eventually thrived to the point where, by the 1960s, the population was big enough to justify an ambitious translocation programme.

Led by the celebrated Ian Player (brother of golfer Gary), the board's teams of rangers and scientists pioneered and perfected drug-darting techniques to capture and move the animals, and the small breeding herds set down in distant places were carefully nurtured until their survival and growth were assured. The white rhino still thrives in the Hluhluwe-Umfolozi park.

The black rhino, too, faced (and still faces) a grim future. Forty years ago just two groups remained in the whole of South Africa; today, the Hluhluwe-Umfolozi serves as home to over 400; other have been dispersed to reserves around the country, and a number flourish under private protection. Several other countries have also launched rhino management programmes. The most successful of these is perhaps Namibia, whose surplus animals provide stock for reserves in neighbouring countries.

SANDGROUSE
Family Pteroclidae

These medium-sized, dove-like birds – southern Africa is home to four species – are nothing much to look at, but they have some very special qualities. In particular, they are remarkable in the way they look after their young.

The birds obtain some moisture from the seeds they eat, but in the drier western regions a daily intake of water is still needed to sustain the chicks. So at nesting time the male ranges far and wide – up to 60 km from the nest – to find water. When he has done so, he soaks his belly and then flies back to his offspring. The chicks drink from the abdominal feathers, which, with their network of tiny, interlocking haired barbs, are designed rather like a sponge and can hold up to 40 millilitres of moisture.

The sandgrouse is also a master of camouflage. When the female sits quietly in the nest – which amounts to little more than a small scrape in the sandy ground – she is virtually invisible to the casual eye. Any movement will betray her presence to hovering hawks and other predators, so she 'freezes'. If you approach, she will reveal herself only at the very last moment, flapping away just before she is trodden on.

SCORPIONS
Families Scorpionidae and Buthidae

Popular belief has it that scorpions perform a 'dance', a ritual display of affection, just before they mate. However, although they do go through a dance-like sequence, it isn't the lighthearted affair it looks like. On the contrary the 'steps' are highly functional, designed to clear the ground of obstacles prior to copulation. The male grasps his partner's pincers and pushes and pulls her, and the to-and-fro movement smooths the ground underfoot.

Scorpions, unlike nearly all the other arthropods, make excellent parents. The babies, usually more than 30 of them, develop in a pouch inside their mother's body and are born live, scrambling up onto her

R

back soon after they emerge. There they remain, in some cases for several seasons, until they reach maturity, at which point they drop off and go their own way. Oddly enough, although the mothers are endearingly attentive towards their young, many species are cannibalistic, other scorpions forming a major part of their diet.

Scorpions, together with the spiders, ticks and mites, are classed as arachnids – they have four pairs of legs as opposed to the insects' three pairs. All are carnivorous – and all can sting, though some are a lot more dangerous than others. They have two pincers for holding their prey, and the long, segmented tail carries a sting which is used to paralyze their victims. They locate their prey through the sensory hairs on their pincers and bodies, supersensitive detectors that can interpret tiny air currents and ground vibrations. Having made the 'kill', they inject a powerful digestive fluid into the victim's body and suck out everything except the skeleton.

Scorpion families

Southern Africa is home to around 200 different species and subspecies of scorpion, most of them residents of the hotter, drier, sandier regions of the subcontinent. They are divided into two main families.

The Scorpionidae have large pincers, slender stings and by and large crush their prey (which usually consists of insects) to death. Their venom is relatively harmless.

Then there are the Buthidae, which are the ones to avoid: they look innocuous enough but the toxin from their thick, powerful stings can be deadly. The most poisonous are those of the genus *Parabuthus*, some of which are able to squirt their poison as far as a metre. *Parabuthus granulosa* is perhaps the deadliest, emerging on hot, windy nights to catch insects and small rodents (it also shows little compunction in eating its own kind).

Scorpions have a remarkably long lifespan, some living for up to 30 years. Some – those of the desert areas of southern Africa – are also able to go without food for up to a year and more, provided they begin their fast in well-fed condition.

SCORPIONFISH
Family Scorpaenidae

Several types of these spiny, often strange looking fish rank among the most dangerous of all marine life forms. Many live on the ocean floor around offshore reefs, lurking in ambush for passing prey, well camouflaged by their colours and by their irregular shapes.

One of the most grotesque members of the family is the rock-like stonefish (*Synanceia verrucosa*), which has a disproportionally large head, squat body and fan-like fins, and whose 13 poisonous, sheathed dorsal spines, erected when the creature is disturbed, can cause hours of excruciating pain (to the point of delirium), occasionally even death, in humans. They inhabit the shallower waters, partially buried in sand and coral debris, and are only too easily overlooked by other marine creatures – and by unwary bathers, divers and snorkellers. Also highly dangerous is its extraordinary cousin the raggedy scorpionfish (*Scorpaenopsis venosa*), whose knobbly, many-planed body blends quite beautifully into its ocean-floor surroundings.

Other family members include the brightly hued firefishes. Both the devil and the broadbarred species, with their red-and-white banded bodies and long, feather-like fins, are visual works of art – but the charm is deceptive: the poison in their spines is extremely toxic.

Even more deadly are certain kinds of cone shellfish, prettily clad creatures armed with tiny, barbed, harpoon-like darts full of powerful venom. Their stings aren't especially painful, but the victim can soon lapse into unconsciousness and die within hours from blood-poisoning (known as toxaemia).

SEA ANEMONES
Order Actiniaria

Few life forms are as gentle looking, or as beautiful, as some of the bright sea anemones you see clinging to the rocks of the shoreline. In reality, though, these pretty little flower-like creatures are voracious carnivores that will eat any small fish careless enough to come too close to the tentacles that surround their mouths.

The victims are paralysed by venom from the stinging cells on the anemone's tentacles before being pushed into its mouth – the only opening on its sac-like body.

Most sea anemones attach themselves to the rocks with their suction discs. When the sea gets rough they contract the tentacles to form a smooth lump, so offering minimum resistance to the surging water.

SEA HORSES
Family Syngnathidae

Among the most dedicated fathers of the natural world is the sea horse, a tiny fish which, with its equine head curved down and its rather stylized posture, looks like something out of a book on medieval heraldry. Extraordinarily, it is the male that becomes 'pregnant' and 'gives birth' to the offspring – or rather, broods the eggs.

S

The female lays her eggs, several thousand of them, directly into a pouch in her partner's belly. He then fertilizes them, feeds the embryos (on fluids from the lining of his pouch) and guards them closely until they are ready for the outside world. At that point he expels them with a series of muscular movements which look just like labour contractions.

Despite its appearance, the sea horse is a true fish, complete with gills. It rarely, though, swims freely in the water but, rather, hides timidly among the plants of the ocean, using its hook-like head to pull itself around and its tail as an anchor.

> *It is the male seahorse that becomes 'pregnant' and 'gives birth' to the offspring – or rather, broods the eggs.*

Southern Africa's waters are home to five different species, all of them rare, the most endangered the Knysna sea horse (*Hippocampus capensis*). Unique to the lagoon area, this little creature is being pushed towards extinction by the degradation of its habitat and by 'collectors' in search of prize additions to their home aquariums. Sea horses generally, moreover, are much in demand in countries in the Far East for their alleged medicinal properties.

SEA SNAKES
Family Elapidae

These snakes are distinctively adapted to life in the ocean waters: they have flattened, oar-like bodies and tails that help them swim, large lungs, valved nostrils, and nasal glands that get rid of excess salt.

Many species are also venomous, and they are a fairly common cause of death in parts of southeast Asia and elsewhere.

Southern African waters are home to just one species, the yellow-bellied sea snake (*Pelamis platurus*), which is occasionally thrown up on beaches and into rock pools by storms on the south and east coasts. And, fortunately, its venom is only mildly toxic, though it is said to cause temporary paralysis. The snake is usually black on top and yellow below, and often has a distinctively mottled black and yellow tail.

SEALS
Families Otariidae and Phocidae

Only one species of these likeable marine mammals permanently inhabits southern Africa's shores: the Cape fur seal gathers in some two dozen colonies scattered around the subcontinent's seaboard from Algoa Bay (Port Elizabeth) westwards and up to Cape Cross in Namibia.

Several other species – crabeater, leopard and southern elephant seals and, especially, the sub-Antarctic fur seals among them – visit our shores as vagrants from their breeding grounds in the southern seas.

> *Seals probably developed from land animals of the inland waters.*

Distant origins

The evolution of seals is a subject of much debate in scientific circles, but it is probable that they developed, over the aeons, from terrestrial animals of the inland waters and thus, to a greater or lesser degree, they remain bound to the land. Indeed the Cape seal spends around a third of its life on *terra firma*.

Of the two broad types, the 'true' or earless seals (Phocidae) are better adapted to life in the water: they have streamlined limbs, flippers that are excellent for swimming but which cannot be turned forwards. Thus they are forced to cover the ground in caterpillar-like, shuffling movements of their sinuous bodies. This kind of seal is thought to have descended from a common otter-like ancestor.

By contrast the eared species (Otariidae), of which the Cape fur seal is one, have pointed little external ears and mobile fore and hind-flippers – well-developed limbs that enable it to both lift its body off the ground and propel it forwards. Eared seals may be descended from an early bear-like animal.

Healthy numbers

Most of the Cape fur seal colonies are found on small offshore islands, but the relatively few mainland groups have almost unlimited space and are much larger – that at Kleinsee on South Africa's west coast numbers between 300 000 and 400 000 individuals; Namibia's Cape Cross colony is about 80 000 strong. Up to the end of the 19th century the fur seal was exploited almost to the point of extinction for its skin and meat, but since 1893, when the species received legal protection, the numbers have increased dramatically – even though around 2,5 million pups were harvested under the government controlled hunting scheme between the years 1900 and 1989. The subcontinent total population now stands at close to two million.

Largest of the occasional visitors to the subcontinent's coasts – indeed

S

the biggest of its kind in the world – is the southern elephant seal, the bulls of which can be up to five metres in length and weigh more than three tonnes (ten times heavier than the females). Most of that mass is blubber, needed for insulation in the bitter cold of the sub-Antarctic winter. The animal, which spends two thirds of its life at sea (nearly half of this time beneath the surface; it may even sleep when diving), is distinguished by its trunk-like snout, an extension of the nostrils that seems to serve little purpose, though it does play a part in sexual display during the breeding season.

SECRETARYBIRD
Sagittarius serpentarius

This species is something of a curiosity among birds of prey: it lives for the most part on the ground, striding the open veld with its head thrust forward, its body rocking from side to side as it hunts for the rodents, lizards and snakes that make up its diet. And it kills its prey (notably reptiles), by furiously stamping its victim to death.

The secretarybird, the only species in its family, usually forages in pairs although large groups – 50 and more – will sometimes gather together at watering points.

Although the black crest-feathers vaguely resemble a row of quill pens stuck behind the ear of a medieval secretary, the bird's common name almost certainly derives from the Arabic words 'saqr-et-tair', meaning 'hunter-bird'.

SHARKS
Selachi

These fish are the most efficient, most feared (though some species are the most docile of the ocean's inhabitants), and among the most ancient of the ocean's predators: they have remained essentially unchanged in form and habit for more than 60 million years – proof positive that they are beautifully adapted to their environment. Many are also superbly designed for hunting, and for killing.

Sharks are different from most other fish in that they are cartilaginous – their skeletons are not of bone but of softer cartilage. Sharks also lack a swimbladder, and they have curious scales quite different from those of other fish, that are composed of small teeth, hence their very rough 'sandpapery' skin. Breeding behaviour, too, is different. While most bony fish spawn eggs, sharks give birth to live young, or special egg cases known as 'mermaid purses' from which the young hatch. In some cases the pups attack and eat each other while still inside the mother – so that only two pups are born, one from each uterus.

Southern Africa's ocean waters are home to 109 known types of shark of which, rather surprisingly, only ten are dangerous to man. They range from the tiny (30-centimetre) pygmy shark to the biggest of all living fishes, the slow-moving, timid, 15-metre whale shark. Their teeth vary from the serrated, triangular daggers of the predator to the minute outgrowths of the plankton-eating basking shark.

sometimes fatally. But its reputation as a compulsive killer is probably much exaggerated: less than one in fifty victims snared by KwaZulu-Natal's anti-shark nets is a great white, and it seems it has been blamed for many an attack made by another species. Needlessly exterminated in the past, it now enjoys official protection, and happily its numbers are increasing.

The white death

One of the largest and most fearsome species is the great white shark (*Carcharodon carcharias*), also known as the 'man-eater' and the 'white death'. Its close but now extinct relative, the Megalodon, grew to 15 metres and was probably the earth's most potent predator.

The great white can reach a length of more than six metres, has a pointed snout, razor-sharp serrated teeth, and a voracious appetite for any kind of flesh, living or dead – and it can bite a man in half (or swallow him whole). This monster is common off the east coast between July and November, in Cape waters from December to March, and it has been known to savage unwary bathers,

Other common sharks are the six-metre blue (potentially dangerous); the smooth hammerhead, its eyes set at the end of grotesque projections on either side of its head ('cheeky', but probably pretty harmless); the short-fin mako, prized as one of the world's tastiest game-fishes (dangerous); the powerful Zambesi shark, fierce, aggressive and often found in the shallow waters of estuaries (very dangerous); the blunt nosed brown shark, which has rather small teeth (probably dangerous) and the ragged-tooth shark, a heavy-bodied, long-toothed fish that also comes close inshore (harmless).

S

Sight, sound and smell

These feared predators of the oceans have a lot more going for them than size, strength and rows of deadly teeth. Although they cannot see colours, their eyes are perhaps ten times more sensitive in dim light than those of humans. They also depend heavily on their acute sense of smell, on their ability to detect vibrations in the water around them, and on their hearing.

In fact a shark can hear, and pinpoint, a struggling fish or other commotion in the water from a distance of nearly two kilometres, smell tiny amounts of blood at 400 metres. When closing in on its victim, though, it is swimming virtually blind (this relates to the membrane that covers the eyes of some species, and the protective eye-sockets of others). At this moment, a remarkable mechanism kicks in, an electrosensor, situated in its snout, that 'feels' the electrical pulses produced by its victim's heartbeat or even by the twitch of a contracting muscle.

SILVER TREE

Leucadendron argenteum

This is the tallest of the protea family in the Western Cape, and among the loveliest and most distinctive of southern Africa's trees. It grows to an average height of 10 metres (16 metres in exceptional cases); its large leaves are a delicate green in colour, and their silvery sheen, imparted by a dense covering of silky hairs, is at its most eye-catching when they shimmer in the Cape breezes.

Legend holds that the tree will only flourish within sight of Table Mountain (its natural distribution is confined to the Cape Peninsula and part of the immediate hinterland), but it has in fact been successfully cultivated in Europe and elsewhere. Quite beautiful specimens can be seen in the Kirstenbosch botanical garden that sprawls over the mountain's lower slopes.

Though fairly easy to grow, the tree seems to be vulnerable, probably to fungal infection: cultivated specimens have a habit of dying suddenly and inexplicably.

SMELLY SHEPHERD'S TREE

Boscia foetida

Some trees depend on insects to spread their pollen, usually attracting them with bright flowers and an abundance of nectar. A few, though, go one stage further in their competition for pollinators. The smelly shepherd's tree is one such: in an amazing evolutionary development, its flowers become pungent with the foul smell of excrement – a magnet for the little scavengers of its habitat.

The species is not the only plant to use this enticement: some members of the tribe Stapelieae, a group of succulents commonly known as carrion flowers, give off the putrescent odour of rotting meat.

Another type of shepherd's tree, *Boscia albitrunca*, plays no such tricks, but it is remarkable nevertheless. Also known as the witgat ('white hole' or 'opening') and a member of the caper family, it ranks as one of the most useful residents of southern Africa's arid areas. Its spreading foliage provides animals with much-needed shade in the very often unbearable heat of the

day, and its often hollow trunk acts as a water-tank, capturing and keeping the rare rainwater.

Parts of the shepherd's tree are used to treat epilepsy, and eye infections in cattle; the roots make a tasty coffee-like drink.

And it has its uses for man, too. The hard white wood can be fashioned into tools and utensils. It is also thought to have medicinal value: an infusion of the leaves is used for eye infections among cattle; extracts from the fruit are said to help in the treatment of epilepsy. The preserved flower-buds are reputed to rival the finest of traditional capers in quality. The roots, when ground and roasted, make a tasty coffee-like drink. They also act as an effective preservative, keeping milk and butter fresh long after they usually begin to deteriorate.

S

SNAKES
Suborder Serpentes

Southern Africa is home to more than 140 different kinds of snake, some 20 of which are dangerous to man. Among the poisonous families are the adders, the sea-snakes and a group (the Elapidae) which embraces the cobras, mambas, coral and garter snakes. Among the non-poisonous types are the python (see page 86), the egg-eaters, the blind snakes and the worm snakes.

> *Back-fanged snakes can be highly venomous, but find it difficult to fasten onto human flesh.*

The effect of snake venom differs with the species, but in general terms it may be neurotoxic (attacking the victim's nervous system and stopping the breathing process), haemotoxic (affecting the blood vessels) or cytotoxic (destroying the body's cells).

The front-fanged species, among which are the mambas, cobras, adders, rinkhals, coral, garter and sea-snakes, pose the greatest risk since they are able to get a good grip. The back-fanged ones rarely cause death or serious injury; although some (like the bird-snake) are highly venomous, their fangs are too awkwardly positioned to fasten on to human flesh (unless it be finger or toe) or to inflict much damage.

Snakes are shy creatures: they will try to slither out of the way when they sense your presence (and should be allowed to do so), only striking if suddenly disturbed or provoked.

SOCIABLE WEAVER
Philetairus socius

When you drive through the hot, arid, lonely vastness of southern Africa's north-western parts you'll often see telephone poles, windmill towers and large camelthorn trees weighed down with enormous, rather untidy structures.

These are the homes of the sociable weavers, built entirely from the straws that the birds gather from the dust-dry veld and knit into an interlocking system of chambers. The entire edifice can weigh up to a tonne, contain a multitude of 'rooms' and provide a comfortable residence for

300 paired birds - a veritable palace. The gigantic nest is a safe refuge, protected against the heat, cold and rain and, if well looked after – and if conditions remain favourable – it can survive intact for decades at a stretch. Interestingly, though, it seems that the birds carry out repairs only when there's a good amount of grass available; in drought-stricken years the nests tend to deteriorate, though some colonies will undertake minimal maintenance with inferior 'dubbeltjie' (acacia) twigs.

Designs for living

The tree-nests are usually sited in the lower branches, where they get the maximum amount of shade. The chambers occupy the bottom part of the structure to make it as difficult as possible for predators, of both the airborne and climbing kind, to reach them. Moreover, by using the camelthorn (and sometimes, in the Kalahari, the shepherd's tree) as their base, the birds are avoiding a major risk: these trees have far-reaching lateral root systems that discourage plant growth on the ground below, and thus they create the natural firebreaks necessary for the tree's, and the nest's, survival.

The nests are superbly insulated. Observations show that while outside temperatures fluctuate by as much as 25° Centigrade between day and night, those inside the structure vary by no more than 6°C, and that they never fall below 15°C in winter or rise above 31°C in summer. To provide even more warmth during the chilly months the birds will huddle together, up to five of them crowding into a single chamber. At other, warmer times each bird will contrive to occupy as much space as possible.

Such a solid and permanent home also gives the weavers a headstart in the breeding stakes: this is a highly opportunistic species – as so many desert life forms have to be if they are to survive the long months of scarcity and take maximum advantage of the short, unpredictable periods of plenty. The weavers can lay their eggs just six days after a rainstorm, which is the shortest response period on record for any desert-adapted bird, and in favourable times will produce up to four broods in a season. The chicks remain in the parental nesting chamber for about three weeks after hatching, by which time they are able to fly.

The weaver's house guests

So well adapted and successful are the weavers that it is no surprise that they attract hangers-on, even some that are wholly unwelcome. The tiny pygmy falcon, for instance, could not survive the rigours of the desert winter without the thermal comforts of a good nest, and it uses the weavers' chambers for warmth. Although these falcons normally feed

S

on lizards and insects, they do occasionally seize a weaver, but this is a surprisingly rare bit of piracy: it simply would not be in the raptor's self-interest to destroy the domestic arrangement on which it own life so clearly depends.

SPIDERS

Class Arachnida

Southern Africa is home to a quite enormous diversity of spiders – around 5 000 species altogether, many of which have yet to be studied and documented. They come in every shape and size, are present in practically every habitat, display a bewildering variety of habit and hunting behaviour.

There are species, like the wolf spider, which 'navigate' by the position of the sun; others 'fish' in the slow-moving waters of swamps; 'fly' through the air on threads of silk, sometimes over immense distances (a method of travel known as 'ballooning') and at great heights. One early study found 1 500 of these tiny aeronauts – belonging to 45 different species – at altitudes of up to 4 600 metres. Other spiders live permanently on the earth's loftiest mountains – some on Mount Everest 6 700 metres above sea level, happily feeding off the insects and plant detritus swept onto the icy slopes by powerful updrafts of air.

Ancient and modern

Basically, though, spiders are divided into two suborders, which differ in the way they breathe and the way they operate their fangs. The larger ground-living and often burrowing Mygalomorpha or ancient spiders (also called 'primitive' spiders) have four lungs, and fangs which strike downwards in pick-axe fashion. The small to medium sized 'modern' Aranoemorpha, on the other hand, have two lungs, supplemented by a network of tiny 'breathing tubes' that convey life-giving air to all parts of the body, and horizontal-working pincer-like fangs.

Most of the former species, the Mygalomorpha, live underground in silk-lined tunnels, where they lie in ambush for their prey. They are hairless and generally referred to as trapdoor spiders. Some of the latter fit their tunnel entrance with a lid which they leave partly open at night, and when a small, unsuspecting creature comes along they pop out and seize it – sometimes with amazing speed: one species takes just 0,03 of a second to launch itself and grab its victim.

Baboon spiders also live underground, in deeper tunnels or under rocks, and differ from true trapdoor species in their hairiness and longer legs. Although they are large and fearsome looking, and will rear up with front legs outstretched when threatened, baboon spiders are not dangerously harmful to man. But its nice to keep your distance: their bite can be very painful.

Spinners and jumpers

The two-lunged Araneomorpha are generally the more versatile of the two types, inhabiting every nook and cranny of garden and veld. Many of them are spinners, fashioning webs that may be triangular, circular, hammock-shaped, dome-shaped or funnel-shaped ending in a tunnel. These spiders catch their prey by waiting, beneath the dome or at the end of the tunnel, until an insect gets caught in the long, sticky strands.

Largest of the Araneomorpha groups are the jumping spiders, most of whom are tiny. They stalk their prey and then flick themselves into the air – they have perfected the science of hydraulics: the movement is activated by a sudden increase in the blood pressure in their legs – and pounce.

These are not, though, the only jumping species. The lynx spider (family Oxyopidae) are so called because they leap at their prey much like a cat does. Almost as acrobatic are the 'dancing white ladies' of the Namib desert, some of which perform a frenzied leaping dance to cow their enemies (these are the Leucorchestris); others (the Carparachne) bend their legs into lateral 'spokes' and, with circus-like flair, cartwheel down the dune-side to escape their persecutors.

Most but not all spiders eat insects. The pirate spiders of the genus *Mimetus* are cannibals who cunningly trick females of other spider species by entering their webs and mimicking the courtship behaviour of their mates. Some actually produce pheromones that match the sex-scents of their intended victims. The genus *Palystes* preys on small lizards; *Thalassius* species float on the surface of ponds to catch tadpoles and small fish, and will even dangle a leg below the surface to attract their prey, which they then grasp and drag out of the water to eat. Other fishermen of the arachnid world use nets, which they weave between their legs and, when an unwary insect passes beneath, stretch their limbs to enlarge the mesh and 'cast' it over the unwary prey.

Among the most remarkable hunters are the bolus spiders, most of which are smallish and spherical in shape. They produce a strong strand of silk (which has a ball of glue at its end); lure the prey within range by means of a false pheromone; whirl

S

the 'lasso' or bolus around much in the manner of a hammer thrower on the athletics field, and hurl it to ensnare the creature.

The golden orb-web weaver spiders (genus *Nephila*) have been known to kill and eat the small birds that become trapped in their huge webs. In fact, bird-eaters rank among the world's largest spiders: one South American species has a body length

> *Some spiders 'navigate' by the position of the sun; others fish in slow-moving waters; still others fly through the air on silken threads.*

of up to nine centimetres and a leg-spread of nearly 30 centimetres (birds, though, feature only occasionally in its diet). The smallest spider yet discovered is a tropical rainforest species that measures just 0,5 millimetres in length.

Dangerous spiders

All these species will bite if threatened, and some of the bites can be painful. In southern Africa, however, only the button or black widow spider (see page 22) and the genus *Sicarius*, which lives in the drylands of Namibia and Northern Cape, are dangerous and occasionally fatal to man. Of the two, the latter is probably the

more venomous. Indeed it may be one of the world's most venomous, but there is very little evidence either way: of the two recorded human victims, one died and the other suffered serious illness. The venom of several other species may cause tissue damage and can even result in the amputation of a limb. Violin and sac spiders inflict a bite that, although barely noticed at the time, produces large, inflamed, swollen areas on the body which can eventually turn into very painful and stubbornly long-lasting ulcers.

SPOTTED HYAENA
Crocuta crocuta

The hyaena has long been a creature of mystery, the object of superstitious fear and much maligned in fable and myth. To some rural people it is the very personification of evil, the harbinger of death, the pack-horse of witches. Reinforcing the image are the sounds it makes, a weird cacophony of whoops, shrieks, laughs, cackles and giggles that hint of madness and chill the heart on moonlit nights. To other folk hyaenas are simply 'disgusting' scavengers, body-snatchers that creep through the darkness in cowardly fashion to feed on the kills of nobler animals.

These preconceptions could not be further from the truth: the hyaena is a quite remarkable species, tough, self-reliant, ingenious, arguably the most accomplished of all carnivores. In some areas – in East Africa and in the dry Kalahari, for example – it kills more than half of its food (the proportion is less in the Kruger National Park, where the ground cover is thicker). It hunts in a group, the dominant female initiating a stampede among or leading the long, energy-sapping chase after a herd of antelope. Invariably, the pack (or clan) cleverly manœuvres to isolate one of the weaker animals and then launches a concerted attack to bring it down.

Eating habits

However, hyaenas spread their options. They are the supreme opportunists of the African veld, taking whatever food presents itself, including small prey down to the size of birds and mice. They do scavenge, of course, though the kills of other carnivores account for a surprisingly small part of their food intake. Most of the carcasses are those of animals that have died from non-violent causes (disease or starvation), which the hyaenas locate with almost uncanny precision, guided to the spot by their superb sense of smell. Special, too, is the strength of their teeth and jaws, which are powerful enough to crush the bones for the rich marrow they contain. Their digestive systems are also incredibly tough, quite able to process the bones themselves.

Resourcefulness, plus well-tuned co-operation within the clan, are the keys to the spotted hyaena's success. Occasionally a pack, for example, will actually rob lions of their kill, harassing and mobbing their much

> *The sounds of the hyaena hint of madness, and chill the heart on moonless nights.*

larger and stronger rivals until the cats retire with what dignity they can muster. Indeed, there are recorded incidents of a lion being chased up a tree and kept there, in terror, by a determined hyaena pack.

The focal point

The heart of the hyaena community is the den, invariably a burrow which it takes over from another animal (usually that most energetic of burrow-builders, the aardvark), which has a spacious entrance that narrows into a tunnel and provides the cubs – which must spend a lot of their time alone while the adults are out looking for food – with security from lions, and other predators.

The den is also the hub of the hyaena's social life, a gathering place where members keep contact, establish their status within the group, and learn about feeding prospects.

S

The clan is a flexible unit, its membership continually changing in size and composition. Females usually stay together more or less permanently, but males come and go as the mood takes them and as feeding opportunities occur.

The greeting ceremony

Popular perception has it that hyaenas are hermaphrodites – a belief that stems from the female's prominent male-like sexual organs. However that may be, the genitals, in both sexes, are central to the vital greeting ceremony: when the animals meet, they stand head to tail and lift their hindlegs, so presenting their most vulnerable parts to the other's deadly jaws. The ritual has no sexual meaning; it is simply a demonstration of mutual trust, reaffirming clan loyalties and cementing the ties between members of an extended family.

SPRINGBOK

Antidorcas marsupialis

One of the more unusual displays of behaviour in the mammal world is the springbok's habit of 'pronking', a graceful, ballet-like routine in which the antelope literally seems to spring, rather like a pogo-stick, across the veld in a series of high (two-metre) leaps. During the sequence the legs are held ramrod-stiff, the head is lowered, the back arched, the hairs of the white rump fluffed out. It's a truly captivating sight – but nobody really knows why the animal does it.

There must be a reason: in the wild kingdom, every physical feature, every dynamic, has a purpose.

Pronking carries the springbok along at a fair pace but not so quickly as a gallop, so simple flight cannot be the motivation. But several other ideas have been suggested. First, the leaps could confuse a hunter, a predator which usually takes its prey at ground level. Then, too, a group of springbok all pronking together might make it difficult for a lion, leopard or spotted hyaena to select a particular individual. The bobbing white rump, moreover, almost certainly acts as an alarm signal, alerting other antelope in the area. It also sends a message to the carnivore, saying 'I've seen you'. Finally, pronking enhances vigilance, giving each member of the herd a clear view of the surrounding countryside and its lurking dangers.

The great migrations

Springbok are residents of the dry, open plains of southern Africa. They are elegant creatures, noted for their soft fawn-and-white colours, delicate features and deeply ringed, quite beautiful lyre-like horns.

They normally live in small herds but when they are on the move to fresh feeding grounds they may come together in massive aggregations – a common enough sight little more than a hundred years ago. Indeed the great springbok treks of the 19th century are the stuff of legend. One observer reported a migration that stretched for 210 kilometres on a 22-kilometre front. Two others – a medical doctor and his companion – tried to quantify a passing parade, calculating that it covered at least 4 000 hectares of Kalahari countryside and that each hectare contained about 20 000 animals so that, by their reckoning, there were 80 million closely packed animals within their sight! This was obviously a gross exaggeration, but the concourse they witnessed was undoubtedly huge.

The springbok no longer move across the veld in such fashion: the vast treks may have been responses to sudden increases in population (perhaps also to drought), and the numbers have since declined – the herds were savagely depleted, before the turn of the last century, by the guns of the settlers, by the great rinderpest epidemic of the 1890s, and above all by the fences the farmers erected.

It is estimated that there are rather more than 100 000 springbok left in the wild, a tiny remnant of the once-great populations. The last of them are to be found in the Kalahari . Others are reared by game-farmers for venison and for the hunting business. Some are bred to produce all-white or all-black animals.

STICK INSECTS
Order Phasmatodea

These curious creatures are perhaps the wild kingdom's most accomplished masters of disguise, their camouflage developed to absolute perfection. They come in a myriad sizes, shapes and colours, but all have one thing in common: their bodies have evolved to imitate the precise vegetation in which they live. Some are identical to leaves; others, covered in bumps and pits and thorny outgrowths, to twigs or tree-bark; still others to stems of grass.

Many species sway gently in the breeze, much as parts of a plant will, and adopt postures that faultlessly fit the background tapestry. Moreover, the female's eggs are often shaped very much like the seeds of the plant on which she feeds. If passive pretence fails, the insects will resort to their final line of defence, suddenly opening their brightly hued hind-wings (which may also have eye-spots) when molested.

S

More than 50 species of stick insect are found in southern Africa, most of them small, a few large. The biggest, *Bactrodema aculiferum*, can reach a full 25 centimetres in length.

TADPOLE SHRIMP
Triops granarius

This tiny creature is one of the few land-living organisms to have survived over the aeons – in this case for more then 300 million years – without undergoing evolutionary change. It is wonderfully adapted in every way to unpredictable conditions, living in temporary rainwater pools of the world's more arid areas – and, in southern Africa, also in mud-wallows, pans and waterholes that often dry out completely.

The shrimp is omnivorous, happy to eat anything from algae and bits of plant matter to other arthropods and even members of its own kind. It has remained in its original form, happy and quite untouched by the earth's great climatic dramas, because it has no predators: the pools last for too short a time to nurture enemies.

For millions of years the shrimp has remained quite untouched by the earth's great dramas.

In the desert areas the shrimp is just one of countless organisms, a vast concourse of near-invisible insects and crustaceans, that the rare rains awaken. Most of them over-winter in the form of eggs, which are tough enough to resist the intense heat and dryness. Indeed, some eggs are able to withstand temperatures close to boiling point! Moreover, they are surprisingly mobile, moving between the various pans and other water sources in the mud stuck to the feet of birds and animals.

TAMPAN TICKS

These tiny, blood-sucking insects, which collect in colonies of thousands, are among the most extraordinary residents of southern Africa's semi-desert regions.

Despite their chosen environment, tampan ticks cannot cope with the high temperatures of the open terrain and retreat into the shaded ground around acacia and other hardy trees, positioning themselves a few centimetres below the surface. There they wait in ambush for the first luckless animal to seek relief in the same cool spot.

The ticks are equipped with sensitive carbon dioxide receptors, and they can also detect movement. As soon as an antelope or large mammal approaches, they make their way to the surface in their multitudes and, guided by their receptors, home in on and fasten themselves to their host to gorge themselves on its blood. Their saliva contains a weak neurotoxin that deadens the flesh, so the victim is quite oblivious of their presence. This lack of awareness can prove fatal to an animal that remains too long in the shade. Cattle have been known to die from exsanguination (the draining of their blood) and from the ulcers that develop from the tick bites.

But as soon as the animal host makes a move to leave, the tampan ticks simply drop off its body – an unusual response among ticks but absolutely essential to this heat-sensitive member of the family.

All of which helps explain why desert animals often choose to shelter from the scorching sun under modest-looking trees and bushes in preference to the large, more invitingly shady specimens.

Visitors to the Kalahari Gemsbok National Park and other dry wildernesses are also at risk: the ticks do not discriminate between mammal species. Be wary: should you choose to cool off beneath the canopy of a thorn tree you'll be inviting a most unwelcome presence.

TERMITES

In parts of southern Africa the veld is studded by hundreds, thousands, of earth structures. These are the homes of the termites, or 'white ants', tiny creatures that are arguably the supreme architects of the wild kingdom.

Termites have been around since the age of the dinosaurs, living in vast colonies that can number a million and more inhabitants, ceaselessly foraging for the dead vegetable matter – leaves, grass, wood – on which they live. In doing so they provide a vital food source for species ranging from lizards to birds and foxes.

The termite colony

The way in which some termites (the Macrotermitinae) prepare their food is a complex and fascinating process. Essentially, they gather cellulose material, or lignin (which other life forms find quite indigestible), take it underground and 'cultivate' a special kind of fungus to break it down, thus releasing the nitrogen, proteins and energy locked into the dead matter. It is a remarkable relationship: the termites cannot absorb the lignin themselves, but pass it out in their waste, depositing it in a 'garden' where the fungus consumes and digests it. The termites then eat the fungus.

Other 'lower' termite species digest cellulose and lignin with the help of microscopic organisms – bacteria and protozoa – which form an ongoing symbiotic relationship with their host, living in its gut and passing down the termite generations through the exchange of fluids.

The termitarium is also special. Its architectural design differs according to the type of termite: some are built under the surface, others above ground in various shapes – domed, steepled, turreted. But all have an infinity of passageways and chambers, all are ventilated by convection-generated air currents, and all maintain constant atmospheric condition.

Just as well organized are the colonies themselves, divided strictly according to function into the queen, who must be constantly and carefully nurtured for only she can mate to produce the coming generations; the soldiers (which defend the nest); the workers (which build and forage), and sexed individuals which, when the weather is exactly right (usually before the summer rains) emerge as winged nymphs (known as alates) and fly off in their myriads in their bid to reproduce. The majority fail, falling victim to predators.

TSAMMA MELON

Citrullus lanatus

This is perhaps the best-known of several extraordinary plants which are vital to the survival of many animal species, and until recently to man himself, in the arid wastelands of the Kalahari. Among the others is the gemsbok cucumber (*Acanthosicyos naudinianus*). Both are rich sources not only of food but of precious moisture.

The tsamma, which looks a bit like a small watermelon growing on a long, trailing stem (and which ripens during the dry winter months), makes rather bland eating and its calorific value is low, but it contains plenty of Vitamin C, some useful trace elements and, most importantly, water. The cucumber's oval-shaped fruit is smaller (and spiny) but it has a huge, fleshy root that penetrates a good metre and more into the sand.

Antelope – springbok, steenbok, gemsbok, eland and hartebeest among them – feed on these plants, as do rodents, insects and carnivores such as jackals, honey badgers and, oddly enough, hyaenas. Several of these mammals cannot digest the whole seeds, which are packed with protein and vegetable fat: their digestive juices merely weaken the outer shells. The animals pass the seeds out in their waste and thus help disperse and propagate the species –

a classic example of the mutual dependence of plant and animal.

For centuries the wild fruits were an essential part of the San (Bushman) survival regime, serving as caches of water and as a valuable, at times life-saving, food source: these hardy desert folk would sometimes live on nothing else for weeks on end. The plants could be eaten raw but were usually cooked beneath a covering of heated sand and ash; the seeds, when roasted (or fried) and ground yield a fairly palatable flour-like substance, and the shell of the melon is sturdy enough to have been used as a pot.

TSESSEBE
Damaliscus lunatus

To the casual observer this large, rather ungainly looking bovid is quite unremarkable, but it does have one very special quality: it is the swiftest of all the region's antelopes, able to run faster, and for longer distances, than a horse.

The tsessebe, which is related to the bontebok and the blesbok, is a reddish-brown animal with long, pointed ears, lyre-shaped horns, dark face and yellow-white markings on the rump. It stands much higher at the withers (shoulders) than at the haunches (rear) – a physical structure that contributes to both its speed and

stamina. An adult can, at the gallop, cover the ground at more than 60 kilometres an hour.

These are grazing animals, found on the grasslands and savanna woodlands of the subcontinent's northern parts. Different races of the same species occur in other parts of Africa, namely the topi in East Africa; the korrigum, which clings to survival in a tiny area of West Africa; and the rather more widespread tiang, resident of a region stretching east from Nigeria to Ethiopia.

TSETSE FLY
Family Glossinidae

For centuries this small, bloodsucking fly has been (and in parts still is) the scourge of sub-Saharan Africa, spreading deadly disease among both man and his cattle, and there have

T

been huge, costly and only partially successful efforts to eradicate it. Yet, judged on its unusual breeding pattern, it seems to be one of the most vulnerable of insects.

The female tsetse fly lives for only six months or so, and during that period she will give birth, at spaced intervals, to no more than ten or 15 larvae, each of which she rears individually and with loving care. Her offspring is large, nearly as big as she is, and (almost unique among the higher insects) she rears it in her uterus, or pouch. While growing there, and after it hatches to become a maggot, the larva 'suckles' from an internal nipple.

The fly lives on blood, and while feeding may transmit a minute blood-parasite (called a trypanosome) to its host. If the latter is human, the parasite will trigger sleeping sickness, or trypanosomiasis, an infection that leads to fever, swollen glands and, eventually, inflammation of the brain and death. Symptoms in the latter stages – which may take years to appear – include a decline in concentration, convulsions, and coma. Death is almost inevitable unless treated, by chemotherapy before the brain is attacked. The equivalent cattle disease is known as nagana. Wild game have become immune to the bite but serve as carriers of the parasite.

There are only about 20 species of tsetse fly, all of which belong to the genus *Glossina*, and they are found only in Africa. They are about the same size as ordinary house-flies, but can be distinguished by their wings, which lie flat across the back when at rest, and by the stout, forward projecting proboscis.

TURTLES
Superfamily Chelonioidea

Few of Nature's larger children have such an arduous breeding programme as the giant sea turtle. Each summer scores of these slow-moving marine reptiles crawl from the ocean to lay their eggs on the beaches of northern KwaZulu-Natal; some have come from as far away as Kenya's Malindi, 3 500 kilometres to the north; others have swum the 2 000 kilometres from the Cape Agulhas area, Africa's southernmost point.

The turtle is one of the gentlest of all creatures, cumbersome, vulnerable, its only defence a hard shell. Yet it has survived almost unchanged in form for close on 100 million years. Largest of the family are the almost two-metre long leatherbacks; slightly smaller are the loggerheads. Other species seen along the coasts are the green turtle and the hawksbill.

The female fly 'suckles' her young from an internal nipple.

The miracle of birth

Leatherbacks and loggerheads have been nesting on these shores for millennia, travelling huge distances to home in, unerringly, on that precise stretch of beach on which they were born – which, in the case of some individuals, could have been 50 years and more in the past.

Studies indicate that the male arrives first; mating takes place a little way offshore, and the female then finds her way through the coral reefs (these are the world's southernmost) and intertidal zone to the beach in search of a scent, a distinctive smell that surrounded her when she herself was a tiny hatchling, and which was programmed into her impulse mechanism. When she finds the exact place, she digs a 60 centimetre deep hole in the sand and drops her clutch of around a hundred soft-shelled eggs, covers them, carefully disguises the nest and then, exhausted, retreats back to the sea.

The female turtle will lay about 500 eggs in a season at intervals of ten days or so, and will come back – perhaps the following year, perhaps not for another ten years – to repeat the process. After 70 days incubating, the babies emerge at nighttime, and run a gauntlet of ghost crabs on the beach to plunge into an even more predator-infested ocean. It is believed that only one of every 500 that manage to reach the water will survive to return to the breeding grounds as an adult.

Escape from oblivion

Despite this huge mortality rate the turtles of the east coast flourished – until they began to fall prey to man's appetites and vanities. Valued for their meat, their eggs and the oil in their bodies, and as talismans and ornamentation, they were killed off in their thousands. By the 1960s they were well on their way to regional

> Some turtles arrive from as far away as Kenya's Malindi, 3 500 kilometres to the north.

extinction. But during that decade the first concerted rescue operation was launched, by the scientists of the Natal Parks Board. Rangers began patrolling the shore; the local village communities pitched in to help; a myriad hatchlings were collected and released. And the turtles began returning – though many scientists believe the effort has been too little and too late.

WARTHOG
Phacochoerus africanus

Of all southern Africa's mammals, the warthog is to human eyes perhaps the ugliest of all. But it has other, admirable qualities: it is tough, courageous, and well adapted to the fairly open savanna and woodland country in which it lives in.

The species is a member of the pig family (Suidae): the males are known as boars, the females as sows, the young as piglets, and a group of warthogs is called a 'sounder'.

The male's 'warts', a pair of large protuberances under the eyes and a more modest pair further down the snout, protect the animal's face when fighting, serving much the same purpose as a cricketer's mask. The female has one, much smaller pair just below her eyes. Hardly more attractive is the long snout, which is bone-hard and used to dig away at the soil in search of roots and tubers, and for clearing earth from the family burrow. In fact the whole of the head – which looks much too large for the body – works as a kind of powerful food-gathering scoop. The big, hard head also plays its part in battles against predators such as cheetah, leopard (the chief enemy), lion and, to a lesser extent, wild dog.

Because its legs are so short, the warthog kneels down when feeding (it eats grass as well as fleshy plant matter) but is not entirely vegetarian. It will feed from carcasses, and indeed has been known to drive predators such as cheetahs and wild dogs away from their kills.

The animal's armoury

The warthog is a dangerous opponent, especially when its young are threatened (it has been known to tree a leopard). The canine teeth, which have developed into long, curved tusks, are highly effective weapons, and are kept razor-sharp by the continual grinding together of the longer (45-centimetre) upper and shorter (15-centimetre) lower pairs. Like all animals, though, the warthog prefers to avoid rather than invite confrontation, and when it senses danger it holds its tail erect, a clear reference point for the rest of the warthog family as they trot swiftly but daintily (and often in strict file) through the long grass in one of the African veld's more comic sequences.

One of the odder elements of the adult warthog's behaviour is the way it enters the burrow – backwards. But this makes sense, because in doing so it covers its rear and any pursuer will have to face its formidable tusks. Its exit from the burrow, often an abandoned and modified aardvark hole, is also unusual: typically there will be an ominous rumble beneath the ground before the animal emerges, in an startling explosion of noise and dust, to race away.

WELWITSCHIA
Welwitschia mirabilis

This plant of the often ferociously hot, barren-seeming wastelands of the Namib desert has evolved in quite bizarre fashion to cope with its harsh environment.

Once described by the great Charles Darwin as 'the platypus of the Plant Kingdom', the welwitschia, a primitive type of conifer, lives for a thousand years and more, but in all that time manages to produce just two leaves! These are long and straggly, and grow continuously from the base, splitting into strips, the outer ribbon-like parts withering before the onslaught of burning sun and driven sand. Some specimens reach a mass of up to 100 kilograms; all have turnip-like stems, tap-roots to absorb what little moisture there is beneath the ground (much of it derived from mist), and leaf-pores that close up during the blistering desert days.

The welwitschia is by no means the only or even the most prominent life form in this desolate region of stony plains and immensely high dunes. Here, in what at first glance seems to be a barren country but is in fact one of the earth's most remarkable living deserts, you'll find a surprisingly rich diversity of species ranging from conventional big game to a fascinating array of small, specialized animals. Some of the life forms – many of the insects, for instance, and the sand-digging and sand-diving lizards – are unique, for this is the world's most ancient desert and the long millennia have given free rein to the evolutionary process.

> *In its thousand and more years of life, the welwitschia plant produces just two leaves.*

Much of the Namib's animal life is nurtured not by rain and ground cover (there are very little of these) but by mists that roll in from the Atlantic Ocean in the west, and by hot breezes (known as berg winds) from the interior that bring in grass segments and other nutritious bits and pieces. Larger game is sustained by the occasional pan and spring.

W

WHALES
Order Cetacea

Humpback whales (see page 58), often seen close inshore along southern Africa's coasts, make long, eerily resonant singing sounds, their 'songs' varied enough for individuals to be recognized. And the sounds, it has been suggested, travel for hundreds of kilometres beneath the sea, and could well represent 'long-distance calls' to each other.

Like the dolphins (see page 38), whales have remarkably sophisticated ways of communicating, of identifying one another, and of navigating routes (by echo-location) through the ocean depths. Each species has its own, often extremely complex repertoire of whistles, moans, grunts, clicks and noises that are sometimes too low in pitch for the human ear to capture. The precise nature of these 'languages', however, are still poorly understood.

Size and origin
Whales are the largest animals to have lived in the annals of the earth, and the biggest of all is the blue whale, a monster that grows to over 30 metres and can weigh 100 tonnes – equivalent in weight to some 25 African bull elephants.

Whales, and indeed all marine mammals, evolved from land animals which, at different times over the past 60 million years, returned to the oceans. Cetaceans (whales and dolphins) are thought to have developed from the same ancestral line as antelope, camels, pigs, cattle and the hippopotamus.

The two main whale groups are the baleens (also known as whaleback whales) and the toothed whales. The former live on minute planktonic organisms such as the shrimplike krill, which they sieve from the water through the baleen plates hanging from the roofs of their mouths. The toothed whale, on the other hand, is a carnivore, living on a variety of prey including fish, squid, octopuses and seabirds.

The killer whale (or orca, of *Free Willy* fame) is technically not a whale but a dolphin. It feeds on other marine mammals (see page 38).

The 'right' whale
Nearly 30 species of whale migrate into and through southern Africa's waters, including the humpback, the blue, the minke, the sei, Bryde's, and the beaked, sperm and pilot whales.

Most notable of all, however — certainly the most visible — is the southern right whale, which comes into the bays of the southern and (less often and in fewer numbers) the western seaboards to mate and to calve from the month of June through to November.

The southern right is a large animal, weighing up to 60 tonnes, and is so named because early whalers considered it the 'right' whale to hunt since it moved slowly enough for rowing boats to approach, its carcass floated, and it produced high yields of oil and baleen. The latter commodity, more commonly known as whalebone, had great commercial value during the 19th century: light, flexible, tough and easily cut, it went into the manufacture of brooms, umbrellas and anything else that demanded strength and elasticity. It was especially prized in the fashion industry, which used it to make corset-stays, hoops for skirts, men's stiff shirt-collars and shoe-horns.

Characteristic features of the southern right are the growths of whitish, hardened skin, called 'callosities', that cover the animal's head and mouth area. The patterns of these vary from animal to animal, so that one can quite easily identify a particular individual (and recognize it on its next visit). At a distance, right whales can also be distinguished from other species by their V-shaped 'blows' – water that is ejected from their blowholes.

At one time the much persecuted southern right population had been brought to the edge of extinction by the whaling industry but, protected by international conservation measures, has staged an excellent recovery. The number off southern Africa's coasts is approaching 2 000, and is doubling every ten years.

WILD DOG
Lycaon pictus

Although a member of the same family (Canidae), the wild dog is not in fact closely related to the domestic animal. For a start, it has four toes on each forefoot and not the usual five. Other distinguishing features are its large, rounded ears, bushy white-tipped tail and black, yellow and white (or 'tortoise-shell') colouring. the wild dog, also known as the Cape hunting dog, is a highly co-operative creature that lives in groups in the savanna woodlands and broken, hilly countryside. It hunts in a packs, running its prey to exhaustion before the final kill.

The wild dog will steal a cheetah's kill, and put a leopard to flight.

W

The sharing instinct

Of all Africa's predators, this animal has perhaps the most intricate social system. Each individual's seniority within the pack, its place in the hunt and its rights to the spoils are subtly and precisely defined. The ranking structure is not permanent: the order changes over the seasons as cubs are born, adults grow old and dominance is challenged. What does remain constant, though, is loyalty to the wider community: group survival is the overriding impetus; all is sacrificed to the wellbeing of the pack as a whole.

> The dog's social system is intricate and subtle: each pack member's seniority, its place in the hunt and right to the spoils are precisely defined.

In the typical wild dog pack the only members allowed to breed are the dominant male and female, the so-called alpha pair. The others forego this privilege and turn their energies to helping in various ways: guarding the den, looking after the pups, bringing chewed and partly digested food back from the kill to regurgitate it – vomit it up – for the youngsters to eat. Until quite recently this was thought to be a fixed pattern of behaviour. During the past few years research has shown, however, that quite often a second female, and even a second male, may breed. The lives of the second mother's offspring, though, are precarious: depending on her mood and on a number of other factors (such as the amount of food available), the alpha female might kill the pups, or take them over as her own, or leave them in peace, or even, rather surprisingly, help her rival raise them.

Hunters supreme

Wild dogs are superb hunters, famed for their tenacity and stamina. Their top running speed is over 60 km/h, and they are able to keep up a steady 45 km/h for about five kilometres.

One or two of the pack members begin the long pursuit while the others follow at leisure, taking over when the leaders tire and, as they come within reach of the quarry, snap away until it falls. Even then, with fresh meat there for the taking, the sharing instinct is strong. Allan Reich, a scientist who studied the dogs of the Kruger National Park, noted on one occasion that the animal that had led the hunt invariably stood back at the carcass. 'All were eating peacefully,' he wrote, 'save for the subordinate male. He had made the kill; he had trotted back to the others; he had let them taste the blood on his mouth, and he had led them back to the kill. Now he waited for what, to our human minds, was rightfully his. He eventually managed a few scraps.... What a remarkable creature!'

The pack's hunting range is huge, covering anything from 500 square kilometres in a relatively confined place like the Kruger to a hefty 2 000 square kilometres in areas where the game migrates. The dogs are always on the move, living a reasonably settled life only during the three-month denning (parenting) period.

The mystery of small numbers

Courage and resourcefulness are other assets. The dogs will chase the fearsome spotted hyaena from a carcass, steal a cheetah's kill, send a leopard scurrying up the nearest tree – and sometimes keep it there for several hours, almost as if they were playing some sort of game.

Yet even with so much going for it – hunting prowess, fearlessness, a co-ordinated lifestyle, the ability to produce plenty of healthy offspring – the wild dog remains among Africa's most endangered animals.

Why this should be so is not fully understood. Admittedly, the species has been savagely persecuted as a threat to both livestock and the game herds. Even in parks and other conservation areas they were shot to death in line with an official carnivore control policy. And, of course, their ranges have been drastically reduced by human settlement. Yet this does not really explain why they are so few in number: in southern Africa, only the Kruger, northern Botswana and Zimbabwe's Hwange National Park sustain reasonably large populations. They are now strictly protected but, still, their future is in jeopardy even in the best managed conservation areas.

Part of the reason may be the wild dog's curiously short span of life (around six years), which may have something to do with inbreeding and the deterioration of the gene pool. Lions also take a heavy toll, especially of the pups. And then there are diseases, some of which (such as distemper and rabies) are inflicted after contact with domestic dogs.

ZEBRAS
Family Equidae

To the casual observer one zebra looks pretty much the same as another, but in fact no two individuals have exactly the same pattern of stripes – and, for that matter, the pattern on one side is different from that on the other. The markings thus serve to 'fingerprint' the animals, enabling the human observer to recognize individuals.

But why exactly these members of the horse family ever evolved stripes in the first place is hard to see: the neat black-and-white markings stand out like beacons against the flat colours of the grassland plains. They certainly don't provide camouflage – though they do tend to confuse lions and other predators, who do not have colour vision and are hard put to single out one individual from the confusion of a herd.

Welcome strangers

A zebra will defend itself by kicking and biting – which is more effective than it sounds: even large carnivores find it difficult to pull down an adult. It also relies on fleetness of foot and stamina, and on its extremely sharp eyesight, hearing and sense of smell. And for this reason it is welcomed into other herbivore communities: you will often see the animal grazing in company with wildebeest, for instance. It's a mutually reward-

ing arrangement: the zebra gains safety in numbers, while the wildebeest benefit from the zebra's ability to give early warning of danger.

No two zebras have exactly the same pattern of stripes.

Zebra types

Southern Africa is home to two species, of which Burchell's or the plains zebra (*Equus burchellii*) is by far the more common. The mountain zebra (*E. zebra*) is a rather smaller animal; its stripes form a 'grid-iron' pattern across the top of its rump, and its dewlap hangs below the throat. Of the latter's two sub-species, the Cape mountain zebra, seriously endangered until fairly recently, is native to the Eastern and Western Cape; Hartmann's mountain zebra inhabits Namibia. Until fairly recently the now-extinct quagga (see page 86), which had stripes only on the front parts of its body, was presumed to have been a third zebra species, but research may indicate that it was merely a subspecies of Burchell's zebra.

Struik Publishers (Pty) Ltd
(a member of The Struik New Holland Publishing Group (Pty) Ltd)
80 McKenzie Street
Cape Town 8001

Reg. No.: 54/00965/07

First published in 1999

3 5 7 9 10 8 6 4 2

Publishing manager: Pippa Parker
Editor: Helena Reid
Assistant editor: Giséle Raad
Designer: Dominic Robson
Illustrator: Danie Jansen van Vuuren

Reproduction by Hirt and Carter (Pty) Ltd, Cape Town
Printed and bound by CTP Press (Pty) Ltd, Cape Town

ISBN: 1 86872 282 1

Cover photographs:
Front cover: Aardvark (N. Dennis), Vygie (L. von Hörsten/SIL),
Elephant (A. Bannister/SIL), Agama Lizard (P. Blackwell/SIL),
Carmine Bee-eater (N. Dennis/SIL), Butterfly (L. Hoffmann/SIL),
Green Mamba (L. Hoffmann/SIL), Daisy (L. Hoffmann/SIL),
Mountain Zebra (N. Dennis/SIL), Caterpillar (L. Hoffmann/SIL).
Back cover: Giraffe (N. Dennis/SIL), Leopard Tortoise
(R. de la Harpe/SIL), Dung Beetles (H. von Hörsten/SIL),
Saddlebilled Stork (N. Dennis/SIL).

SIL = Struik Image Library